Advancing Maths for AQA

Revise for CORE 3

Sam Boardman   Tony Clough

Series editors
Sam Boardman   **Roger Williamson**   **Ted Graham**

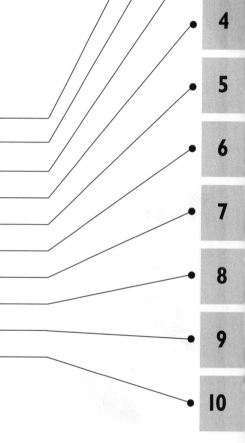

www.heinemann.co.uk
✓ Free online support
✓ Useful weblinks
✓ 24 hour online ordering

01865 888058

Inspiring generations

Heinemann is an imprint of Pearson Education Limited, a company incorporated in
England and Wales, having its registered office at Edinburgh Gate, Harlow,
Essex, CM20 2JE. Registered company number: 872828

www.heinemann.co.uk

Heinemann is a registered trademark of
Pearson Education Limited

First published 2006

11 10
10 9 8 7 6 5 4 3 2

British Library Cataloguing in Publication Data is available from the British
Library on request.

ISBN 978-0435513580

Typeset and illustrated by Tek-Art
Original illustrations © Tek-Art
Cover design by mccdesign ltd.
Printed in Malaysia, CTP-KHL

About this book

This book is designed to help you get your best possible grade in your Pure Core Maths 3 examination. The authors are Principal and Core examiners, and have a good understanding of AQA's requirements.

Revise for Core 3 covers the key topics that are tested in the Core 3 exam paper. You can use this book to help you revise at the end of your course, or you can use it throughout your course alongside the course textbook, *Advancing Maths for AQA AS & A level Pure Core Maths 3 & 4*, which provides complete coverage of the syllabus.

Helping you prepare for your exam

To help you prepare, each topic offers you:

- **Key points to remember** – summarise the mathematical ideas you need to know and be able to use.

- **Worked examples** – help you understand and remember important methods, and show you how to set out your answers clearly.

- **Revision exercises** – help you practise using these important methods to solve problems. Exam-level questions are included so you can be sure you are reaching the right standard, and answers are given at the back of the book so you can assess your progress.

- **Test Yourself questions** – help you see where you need extra revision and practice. If you do need extra help, they show you where to look in the *Advancing Maths for AQA AS & A level Pure Core Maths 3 & 4* textbook and which example to refer to in this book.

Exam practice and advice on revising

Examination style paper – this paper at the end of the book provides a set of questions of examination standard. It gives you an opportunity to practise taking a complete exam before you meet the real thing. The answers are given at the back of the book.

How to revise – for advice on revising before the exam, read the *How to revise* section on the next page.

How to revise using this book

Making the best use of your revision time

The topics in this book have been arranged in a logical sequence so you can work your way through them from beginning to end. But **how** you work on them depends on how much time there is between now and your examination.

If you have plenty of time before the exam then you can **work through each topic in turn**, covering the key points and worked examples before doing the revision exercises and Test Yourself questions.

If you are short of time then you can **work through the Test Yourself sections** first, to help you see which topics you need to do further work on.

However much time you have to revise, make sure you break your revision into short blocks of about 40 minutes, separated by five- or ten-minute breaks. Nobody can study effectively for hours without a break.

Using the Test Yourself sections

Each Test Yourself section provides a set of key questions. Try each question:

- If you can do it and get the correct answer, then move on to the next topic. Come back to this topic later to consolidate your knowledge and understanding by working through the key points, worked examples and revision exercises.

- If you cannot do the question, or get an incorrect answer or part answer, then work through the key points, worked examples and revision exercises before trying the Test Yourself questions again. If you need more help, the cross-references beside each Test Yourself question show you where to find relevant information in the *Advancing Maths for AQA AS & A level Pure Core Maths 3 & 4* textbook and which example in *Revise for C3* to refer to.

Reviewing the key points

Most of the key points are straightforward ideas that you can learn: try to understand each one. Imagine explaining each idea to a friend in your own words, and say it out loud as you do so. This is a better way of making the ideas stick than just reading them silently from the page.

As you work through the book, remember to go back over key points from earlier topics at least once a week. This will help you to remember them in the exam.

CHAPTER 1

Functions

Key points to remember

1 A function is a one-one or a many-one mapping.

2 The set of numbers for which a function is defined is called the **domain**.

3 A function f consists of two things
- a defining rule such as $f(x) = x^2 + 3$
- its domain

4 The set of values the function takes for the given domain is called the **range**.

5 When the domain of f is a continuous interval, the range can be found by considering the graph of $y = f(x)$. The range consists of the possible values that y can take. The range of f is written as an inequality involving $f(x)$.

6 The composite function fg means first g then f, since $fg(x) = f[g(x)]$.

7 A function f has an inverse only when f is one-one. Its graph is obtained by reflecting the graph of $y = f(x)$ in the line $y = x$.

8 A reverse flow diagram can be used to find an inverse function when x occurs only once in $f(x)$. You consider how $f(x)$ has been constructed as a sequence of simple operations and set up a flow diagram. Then you reverse each operation and reverse the direction of the flow to find $f^{-1}(x)$.

9 The inverse of f can be found by the following procedure:
Write $y = f(x)$
- Rearrange the equation to make x the new subject.
- Interchange x and y (equivalent to reflecting in $y = x$)
- The new expression for y is equal to $f^{-1}(x)$.

Worked example 1

The function f has domain $-1 \leqslant x \leqslant 2$ and is defined by $f(x) = 3x^2 - 7$.

(a) Sketch the graph of $y = f(x)$.

(b) Find the range of f.

(a) $y = 3x^2 - 7$ has a ∪ shaped quadratic graph

> The required graph is only part of this parabola.

You need to calculate a few values of f(x)
$$f(-1) = 3 \times (-1)^2 - 7 = 3 - 7 = -4$$
$$f(0) = 0 - 7 = -7$$
$$f(2) = 3 \times (-2)^2 = 12 - 7 = 5$$

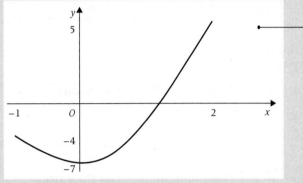

> It is important that the graph is ONLY drawn for values of x between -1 and 2. You may wish to mark the end points of the graph with their coordinates, namely $(-1, -4)$ and $(2, 5)$ or make these coordinates clear by marking the values on the axes.

(b) To find the range of f, you need to find the possible values of y on the graph. The least value of y is -7 and the greatest value of y is 5 for the given domain.

> Using **4**

Range is $-7 \leqslant f(x) \leqslant 5$.

> Using **5**

Worked example 2

The function g is defined for all real values of x by
$$g(x) = (x - 2)^4 - 5.$$
(a) Find **(i)** g(1) **(ii)** g(2) **(iii)** g(3)
(b) State the range of g.
(c) Determine whether the inverse function g^{-1} exists.

(a) **(i)** $\quad g(1) = (-1)^4 - 5 = 1 - 5 = -4$
(ii) $\quad g(2) = 0 - 5 = -5$
(iii) $\quad g(3) = 1 - 5 = -4$
(b) The least value of the function occurs when $x = 2$ and
$g(2) = -5$
The range is $g(x) \geqslant -5$.

> Using **5**

(c) Since g(1) has the same value as g(3), the function g is many-one.
Hence, the inverse function g^{-1} does not exist.

> Using **7**

Worked example 3

The functions f and g are defined with their respective domains by

$$f(x) = 3x + 2, \text{ for all real values of } x$$

$$g(x) = \frac{6}{x - 1}, \text{ for real values of } x, x \neq 1$$

The composite function gf is denoted by h.

(a) Find h(x), in its simplest form.

(b) State the greatest possible domain of h.

(a) $h(x) = g[f(x)] = g(3x + 2) = \dfrac{6}{(3x + 2) - 1}$ ← Using **6**

Hence $h(x) = \dfrac{6}{3x + 1}$. ← You can see from the denominator of h(x) that the value $-\frac{1}{3}$ cannot be part of the domain of h.

(b) Since the domain of g is real values of x, $x \neq 1$, it is necessary to find any values of x that must be excluded from the domain of f, in order to find the domain of h.

Solving $f(x) = 1$ gives $3x + 2 = 1 \Rightarrow x = -\dfrac{1}{3}$ so the

value $-\dfrac{1}{3}$ must be excluded from the domain of h.

The greatest possible domain of h is the real values of x,

$x \neq -\dfrac{1}{3}$.

Worked example 4

The function f is defined by

$$f(x) = \frac{x + 8}{x + 3}, \text{ for real values of } x, x \neq -3$$

(a) The inverse of f is f^{-1}. Find an expression for $f^{-1}(x)$.

(b)　**(i)** Explain why the equation $f^{-1}(x) = f(x)$ has the same solutions as the equation $x = f(x)$.

　　　(ii) Solve the equation $f^{-1}(x) = f(x)$.

Write $y = \dfrac{x + 8}{x + 3}$ and make x the new subject ← Using **9**

$$y(x + 3) = x + 8 \quad \Rightarrow xy + 3y = x + 8$$
$$3y - 8 = x - xy \quad \Rightarrow \quad 3y - 8 = x(1 - y)$$

Hence $x = \dfrac{3y - 8}{1 - y}$

Interchanging x and y gives $y = \dfrac{3x - 8}{1 - x}$

Therefore, $f^{-1}(x) = \dfrac{3x - 8}{1 - x}$.

(b) **(i)** Since the graphs of $y = f(x)$ and $y = f^{-1}(x)$ are obtained from each other by reflection in the line $y = x$, the two graphs must intersect on the line $y = x$. Therefore, each of the equations below must have the same solutions:
$f^{-1}(x) = f(x)$; $f^{-1}(x) = x$; $x = f(x)$.

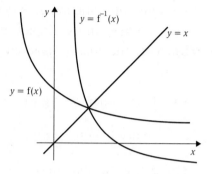

(ii) It is easier to solve $x = f(x)$ which must have the same solutions as $f^{-1}(x) = f(x)$.

Solving $x = \dfrac{x + 8}{x + 3} \Rightarrow x(x + 3) = x + 8$

Rearranging gives $x^2 + 2x - 8 = 0$
Factorising gives $(x + 4)(x - 2) = 0$
Hence $x = -4$, $x = 2$ are the two solutions.

REVISION EXERCISE I

1 The function f is defined for all real values of x by

$$f(x) = \frac{12}{3 + x^2}.$$

Find **(a)** $f(3)$ **(b)** $f(-1)$ **(c)** $f(\sqrt{a})$.

2 The functions f and g are defined for all real values of x by
$f(x) = 3x^2 - 4$ and $g(x) = 5x - 6$.
(a) Find $f(-2)$ and $g(0.2)$.
(b) Find the two values of x for which $f(x) = g(x)$.

3 The function h has domain $-2 \leqslant x \leqslant 3$ and is defined by $h(x) = x^2 - 4$.
(a) Sketch the graph of $y = h(x)$.
(b) Find the range of h.

4 The function p with domain $x \geqslant 1$ is defined by $p(x) = 4 + \dfrac{2}{x}$.
(a) Sketch the graph of $y = p(x)$.
(b) Find the range of p.

5 The function f with domain $0 \leqslant x \leqslant \pi$ is defined by

$$f(x) = \sin\left(x - \frac{\pi}{6}\right).$$

Sketch the graph of $y = f(x)$ and find the range of f.

6 The function g with domain $0° \leqslant x \leqslant 15°$ is defined by
$$g(x) = 2\tan 3x.$$
Sketch the graph of $y = g(x)$ and find the range of g.

7 The functions f and g are defined for all real values of x by
$$f(x) = x + 3 \text{ and } g(x) = x^2 - 1.$$
  (a) The composite function fg, defined for all real values of x, is denoted by h.
    (i) Find $h(x)$.
    (ii) Find the range of h.
  (b) The composite function gf is defined for all real values of x and denoted by p.
    (i) Find $p(x)$.
    (ii) Find the range of p.

8 (a) The function f is defined for all real values of x by $f(x) = x^2 + 3$. Explain why f does not have an inverse.
  (b) The function g is defined for $x > 2$ by $g(x) = x^2 + 3$.
    (i) Explain why g does have an inverse, g^{-1}, and find $g^{-1}(x)$.
    (ii) State the domain of g^{-1}.

9 The functions f and g are defined with their respective domains by
$$f(x) = x - 5, \text{ for all real values of } x$$
$$g(x) = \frac{4}{x + 2}, \text{ for real values of } x, x \neq -2$$

The composite function fg, defined for real values of x, $x \neq -2$ is denoted by h.
  (a) Find $h(x)$.
  (b) **(i)** Find $h^{-1}(x)$ where h^{-1} is the inverse of h.
    (ii) Find the range of h^{-1}.

10 The functions f and g are defined with their respective domains by
$$f(x) = \frac{4}{x + 3}, \text{ for real values of } x, x \neq -3$$
$$g(x) = \frac{3x + 4}{x - 2}, \text{ for real values of } x, x \neq 2$$
  (a) Find expressions for $f^{-1}(x)$ and $g^{-1}(x)$.
  (b) Solve the equation $f^{-1}(x) = f(x)$.
  (c) **(i)** State the range of f and the domain of f^{-1}.
    (ii) State the range of g and the domain of g^{-1}.
  (d) Find $fg(x)$, simplifying your answer.

11 The functions f and g are defined with their respective domains by

$$f(x) = 5 - x^2, \text{ for all real values of } x$$

$$g(x) = \frac{2}{x - 4}, \text{ for real values of } x, x \neq 4$$

(a) (i) Find the range of f.

(ii) Explain whether f has an inverse or not.

(b) The inverse of g is g^{-1}. Find $g^{-1}(x)$ and state the range of g^{-1}.

(c) The composite function gf is denoted by h.

(i) Find h(x), simplifying your answer.

(ii) State the greatest possible domain of h.

12 The functions f and g are defined with their respective domains by

$$f(x) = 2x - 3, \text{ for all real values of } x$$

$$g(x) = \frac{6}{3x - 2}, \text{ for real values of } x, x \neq \frac{2}{3}$$

The composite function fg is denoted by h and the domain of h is $x > 1$.

(a) Find h(x).

(b) (i) Find $h^{-1}(x)$ where h^{-1} is the inverse of h.

(ii) Find the range of h^{-1}.

13 The function f is defined for $x < 0$ by $f(x) = 3x^2 - 2$.

(a) Sketch the graph of $y = f(x)$

(b) (i) Explain why the inverse function f^{-1} exists and sketch the graph of $y = f^{-1}(x)$

(ii) Find an expression for $f^{-1}(x)$.

14 The functions f and g are defined with their respective domains by

$$f(x) = 9 - 5x, \text{ for all real values of } x$$

$$g(x) = \frac{1}{x - 3}, \text{ for real values of } x, x \neq 3$$

The composite function fg is denoted by h.

(a) (i) Find h(x).

(ii) State the maximum possible domain of h.

(b) The inverse of g is g^{-1}.

(i) Show that $g^{-1}(x) = \frac{1}{x} + 3$.

(ii) State the domain of g^{-1}.

(c) Solve the equation $g^{-1}(x) = f(x)$.

Test yourself	What to review
	If your answer is incorrect:

1 The function f is defined for all real values of x by

$f(x) = \dfrac{3}{x^2 + 2}$. Find

    (a) f(0)   **(b)** f(−1)   **(c)** $f(\sqrt{7})$.

Review Advancing Maths for AQA C3C4 pages 1–8.

---

2 Find the range of the function f with domain $-1 \leqslant x \leqslant 2$ and defined by $f(x) = 6 - x^2$.

Review Advancing Maths for AQA C3C4 pages 6–7.

---

3 The functions f and g are defined for all real values of x by $f(x) = x - 4$ and $g(x) = x^2 + 3$. The composite function fg is denoted by h and is defined for all real values of x.
    (a) Find h(x).
    (b) Find the range of h.

Review Advancing Maths for AQA C3C4 pages 1–8.

---

4 The function f with domain $x < -1$ is defined by
        $f(x) = 5 - 2x^3$.
    (a) Find the range of f.
    (b) The inverse of f is f^{-1}.
        Find an expression for $f^{-1}(x)$.

Review Advancing Maths for AQA C3C4 pages 12–15.

---

5 The function g is defined for real values of x, $x \neq 3$

by $g(x) = \dfrac{4x - 1}{x - 3}$ and the inverse of g is g^{-1}.

Find an expression for $g^{-1}(x)$.

Review Advancing Maths for AQA C3C4 pages 12–15.

Test yourself ANSWERS

5 $\dfrac{3x - 1}{x - 4}$

4 (a) $f(x) > 7$ **(b)** $\sqrt[3]{\dfrac{5 - x}{2}}$

3 (a) $h(x) = x^2 - 1$ **(b)** $h(x) \geqslant -1$

2 $2 \leqslant f(x) \leqslant 6$

1 (a) $\dfrac{3}{2}$ **(b)** 1   **(c)** $\dfrac{1}{3}$

CHAPTER 2

Transformations of graphs and the modulus function

Key points to remember

1 A translation of $\begin{bmatrix} a \\ b \end{bmatrix}$ transforms the graph of $y = f(x)$ into the graph of $y = f(x - a) + b$.

2 The graph of $y = f(x)$ is transformed into the graph of $y = -f(x)$ by a reflection in the line $y = 0$ (the x-axis).

3 The graph of $y = f(x)$ transformed into the graph of $y = f(-x)$ by a reflection in the line $x = 0$ (the y-axis).

4 The graph of $y = f(x)$ is transformed into the graph of $y = df(x)$ by a stretch of scale factor d in the y-direction.

5 The graph of $y = f(x)$ is transformed into the graph of $y = f\left(\dfrac{x}{c}\right)$ by a stretch of scale factor c in the x-direction.

6 The **modulus function** $|x|$ is defined by

$$|x| = \begin{cases} x & \text{when } x \geq 0 \\ -x & \text{when } x < 0 \end{cases}$$

Worked example 1

Find the equation of the resulting curve after the curve

(a) $y = x^2$ is translated through $\begin{bmatrix} -1 \\ 5 \end{bmatrix}$;

(b) $y = \cos x$ is stretched in the y-direction by scale factor 5 and stretched in the x-direction by scale factor 2;

(c) $y = 3^x$ is reflected in the y-axis and then translated by $\begin{bmatrix} 2 \\ 0 \end{bmatrix}$.

2

(a) The new curve has equation $y = [x - (-1)]^2 + 5$

$\qquad$ which simplifies to $y = (x + 1)^2 + 5$

$\qquad$ You can multiply out to obtain $y = x^2 + 2x + 6$.

> Using **1**

> This is perfectly acceptable as a final answer.

(b) Stretching by scale factor 5 in the *y*-direction

$\qquad$ $y = \cos x$ is transformed into $y = 5\cos x$

> Using **4**

$\qquad$ Stretching the new curve by scale factor 2 in the *x*-direction

$\qquad$ $y = 5\cos x$ is transformed into $y = 5\cos\left(\dfrac{x}{2}\right)$

> Using **5**

(c) When $y = 3^x$ is reflected in the *y*-axis, the new curve has equation $y = 3^{-x}$.

> Using **3**

$\qquad$ Translating the new curve by $\begin{bmatrix} 2 \\ 0 \end{bmatrix}$ results in the curve with equation $y = 3^{-(x-2)}$.

> Using **1**

$\qquad$ The final equation could be expressed in various ways such as $y = 3^{2-x}$ or $y = \dfrac{9}{3^x}$ and you need to understand why these different forms of the equation are equivalent.

Worked example 2

Find a sequence of geometrical transformations that would transform the graph of

(a) $y = x^3$ into the graph of $y = 3(x + 2)^3$;

(b) $y = 3x^4$ into the graph of $y = x^4 + 5$.

(a) The graph of $y = x^3$ is transformed into $y = (x + 2)^3$ by means of a translation of $\begin{bmatrix} -2 \\ 0 \end{bmatrix}$.

> Using **1**

$\qquad$ The curve $y = (x + 2)^3$ is transformed into $y = 3(x + 2)^3$ by means of a stretch of scale factor 3 in the *y*-direction.

> Using **4**

$\qquad$ The sequence of transformations is a translation of $\begin{bmatrix} -2 \\ 0 \end{bmatrix}$ followed by a stretch of scale factor 3 in the *y*-direction.

> In this case transformations could have been applied in any order.

(b) The graph of $y = 3x^4$ is transformed into $y = x^4$ by means of a stretch of scale factor $\dfrac{1}{3}$ in the *y*-direction.

> Using **4**

$\qquad$ The graph of $y = x^4$ is transformed into $y = x^4 + 5$ by means of a translation of $\begin{bmatrix} 0 \\ 5 \end{bmatrix}$.

> Using **1**

> The sequence of transformations is a stretch of scale
> factor $\frac{1}{3}$ in the y-direction followed by a translation
> of $\begin{bmatrix} 0 \\ 5 \end{bmatrix}$.

> In this case the transformations must be applied in this order.

Worked example 3

(a) The function f is defined for all real values of
   x by $f(x) = |9 - x^2|$
   (i) Sketch the graph of $y = f(x)$.
   (ii) State the range of f.
(b) Solve $|9 - x^2| = 5$.
(c) Hence, or otherwise, solve $|9 - x^2| > 5$.

(a) (i) It is helpful to sketch $y = 9 - x^2$ first

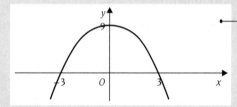

> A useful strategy when sketching graphs involving modulus functions is to consider the corresponding graph with no modulus signs.

Therefore the graph of $y = |9 - x^2|$ is

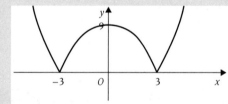

   (ii) The y values of the graph of $y = f(x)$ are never negative.
   The range is $f(x) \geqslant 0$.

(b) The line $y = 5$ would cut the graph of $y = |9 - x^2|$ in 4 distinct points.

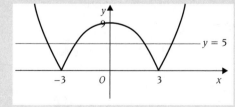

You should now realise that the equation $|9 - x^2| = 5$ has 4 real roots.

Firstly, $9 - x^2 = 5 \Rightarrow x^2 = 4 \Rightarrow x = \pm 2$

Also other roots are found by writing $9 - x^2 = -5$

$9 - x^2 = -5 \Rightarrow x^2 = 14 \Rightarrow x = \pm\sqrt{14}$

The four solutions are $-\sqrt{14}, -2, 2, \sqrt{14}$.

> For $9 - x^2 < 0$
> $|9 - x^2| = -(9 - x^2)$

2

(c) You can use the sketch in part **(b)** to write down the solution to $|9 - x^2| > 5$.

The answer is the three intervals

$$x < -\sqrt{14}, \ -2 < x < 2, \ x > \sqrt{14}$$

> Since you have already found the four critical points $-\sqrt{14}, -2, 2$ and $\sqrt{14}$ you need to see when the y-value of the curve is greater than 5.

Worked example 4

(a) Sketch the graph of $y = |x^2 + 3x|$.

(b) **(i)** Solve the equation $|x^2 + 3x| = 4x + 6$.

(ii) Solve the inequality $|x^2 + 3x| > 4x + 6$.

(a)

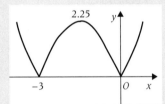

(b) **(i)** The line $y = 4x + 6$ will cross the graph above in two points.

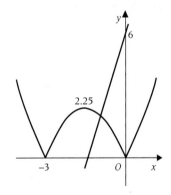

Solving $x^2 + 3x = 4x + 6 \Rightarrow x^2 - x - 6 = 0$.

$(x - 3)(x + 2) = 0 \Rightarrow x = 3, \ x = -2$.

But $x = -2$ does not satisfy the equation $|x^2 + 3x| = 4x + 6$ and so this solution must be rejected.

Solving $x^2 + 3x = -4x - 6 \Rightarrow x^2 + 7x + 6 = 0$.

$(x + 1)(x + 6) = 0 \Rightarrow x = -6, x = -1$.

But $x = -6$ does not satisfy $|x^2 + 3x| = 4x + 6$ and so this solution must be rejected.

The two solutions are $x = -1, \ x = 3$.

(ii) From the graph, $|x^2 + 3x| > 4x + 6$ when $x < -1$, or $x > 3$.

Worked example 5

(a) Sketch on the same axes

   (i) $y = |1 + x|$

   (ii) $y = |3x| - 2$

(b) Solve $|1 + x| = |3x| - 2$.

(c) Solve $|1 + x| > |3x| - 2$.

(a)

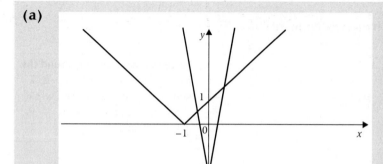

(b) To solve $|1 + x| = |3x| - 2$, several equations have to be considered

$$1 + x = 3x - 2 \quad \Rightarrow 3 = 2x \quad \Rightarrow x = \frac{3}{2}.$$

> This solution satisfies the original equation.

Now consider

$$-1 - x = 3x - 2 \quad \Rightarrow 1 = 4x \quad \Rightarrow x = \frac{1}{4}.$$

But this solution does not satisfy the original equation.
Now consider

$$1 + x = -3x - 2 \quad \Rightarrow 4x = -1 \quad \Rightarrow x = -\frac{1}{4}.$$

But this solution does not satisfy the original equation.
Finally consider

$$-1 - x = -3x - 2 \quad \Rightarrow 2x = -1 \quad \Rightarrow x = -\frac{1}{2}.$$

> This solution satisfies the original equation.

The two solutions are $x = \frac{3}{2}$, $x = -\frac{1}{2}$

(c) Using the graph, $|1 + x| > |3x| - 2$

$$\text{has solution} -\frac{1}{2} < x < \frac{3}{2}.$$

> Consider when the graph of $y = |1 + x|$ is higher than the graph of $y = |3x| - 2$.

REVISION EXERCISE 2

1 Find the equation of the resulting curve after the curve

  (a) $y = x^3$ is translated through $\begin{bmatrix} 3 \\ 2 \end{bmatrix}$;

  (b) $y = \sin x$ is translated by 1 unit in the y-direction then stretched in the x-direction by scale factor 3;

  (c) $y = 2^x$ is reflected in the x-axis and then translated by $\begin{bmatrix} -1 \\ 0 \end{bmatrix}$.

2 Describe a sequence of geometrical transformations which map the graph of

  (a) $y = \tan x$ onto the graph of $y = 3\tan 2x$;

  (b) $y = x^2$ onto the graph of $y = x^2 - 2x + 5$;

  (c) $y = 9^x$ onto the graph of $y = 2 + 3^x$.

3 Find a sequence of geometrical transformations that would map the graph of

  (a) $y = x^5$ onto the graph of $y = 4(x - 1)^5$;

  (b) $y = 5x^2 - 7$ onto the graph of $y = x^2$.

4 Describe geometrically how the curve $y = 8^{x+1}$ can be transformed into the curve $y = 2^x$ by a sequence of transformations.

5 Find a sequence of geometrical transformations that would map the graph of $y = 2 + \sin 3x$ onto the graph of $y = 4\sin 3x$.

6 Sketch the graphs of **(a)** $y = |x - 2|$; **(b)** $y = |3x|$;
    (c) $y = 4 + |x|$; **(d)** $y = 5 - |x|$.

7 Sketch the graphs of **(a)** $y = 2 + |3\cos x|$;
    (b) $y = |2 + 3\cos x|$ for $0 \leqslant x \leqslant 2\pi$.

8 **(a)** Sketch the graph of $y = |8 - x^2|$.
  (b) Solve the equation $|8 - x^2| = 4$.

9 Solve the equations **(a)** $|5 - 2x| = x + 3$ **(b)** $|5x^2 - 2| = 3x$.

10 **(a)** Sketch the graph of $y = |16 - x^2|$.
  (b) Solve $|16 - x^2| = 7$.
  (c) Hence, or otherwise, solve $|16 - x^2| > 7$.

11 (a) Sketch the graph of $y = |x^2 - 4x|$.
   (b) (i) Solve the equation $|x^2 - 4x| = 3x - 6$.
      (ii) Solve the inequality $|x^2 - 4x| < 3x - 6$.

12 (a) Sketch on the same axes (i) $y = |4 - x|$ (ii) $y = |2x| - 5$.
   (b) Solve $|4 - x| = |2x| - 5$.
   (c) Solve $|4 - x| > |2x| - 5$.

13 The functions f and g are defined for all real values of x by
$$f(x) = |x - 3|, \qquad g(x) = x^2 + 1.$$
   (a) Find the range of f and the range of g.
   (b) Determine whether the inverses of f and g exist.
   (c) The composite function fg is defined for all real values of x and is denoted by h.
      (i) Find $h(x)$.
      (ii) Solve the equation $h(x) = 1$.
   (d) Solve the inequality $f(x) > g(x)$.

Test yourself	What to review
	If your answer is incorrect:
1 Describe geometrically how the curve: (a) $y = x^2$ is transformed into the curve $y = (x - 2)^2 - 8$ (b) $y = \sin x$ is transformed into the curve $y = \sin 4x$	Review Advancing Maths for AQA C3C4 pages 23–25.
2 Describe a sequence of geometrical transformations which transforms the graph of (a) $y = \tan x$ into the graph of $y = -\tan 3x$; (b) $y = x^5$ into the graph of $y = 4(x - 7)^5$; (c) $y = 4^x$ into the graph of $y = 3 + 2^x$.	Review Advancing Maths for AQA C3C4 pages 23–25.
3 (a) Sketch the graph of $y = 1 - x^2$. (b) Hence sketch the graph of $y = |1 - x^2|$. (c) Solve the equation $4|1 - x^2| = 3$.	Review Advancing Maths for AQA C3C4 pages 29–35.
4 Solve the inequality $|14 - x^3| < 13$.	Review Advancing Maths for AQA C3C4 pages 35–37.
5 Solve $|3x + 2| < |x| + 6$	Review Advancing Maths for AQA C3C4 pages 35–37.

1 **(a)** Translation of $\begin{bmatrix} 2 \\ -8 \end{bmatrix}$ **(b)** Stretch of SF $\frac{1}{4}$ in x-direction

2 **(a)** Reflection in x-axis; stretch of SF $\frac{1}{3}$ in x-direction.

(b) Translation of $\begin{bmatrix} 7 \\ 0 \end{bmatrix}$; stretch of SF 4 in y-direction.

(c) Translation of $\begin{bmatrix} 0 \\ 3 \end{bmatrix}$; stretch of SF 2 in x-direction.

3 **(a)**   **(b)**

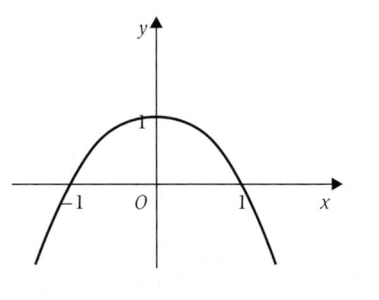

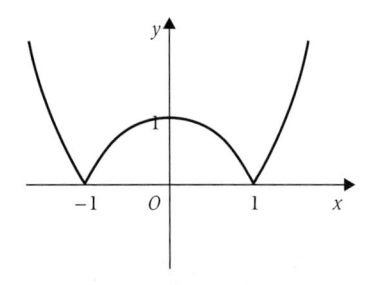

(c) $-\dfrac{\sqrt{7}}{2}, -\dfrac{1}{2}, \dfrac{1}{2}, \dfrac{\sqrt{7}}{2},$

4 $1 < x < 3$

5 $-4 < x < 2$

CHAPTER 3

Inverse trigonometric functions and secant, cosecant and cotangent

Key points to remember

1 $\sin^{-1} x$ has domain $-1 \leqslant x \leqslant 1$ and range

$-\dfrac{\pi}{2} \leqslant \sin^{-1} x \leqslant \dfrac{\pi}{2}$.

The graph of $y = \sin^{-1} x$, $-1 \leqslant x \leqslant 1$ is obtained by

reflecting the graph of $y = \sin x$, $-\dfrac{\pi}{2} \leqslant x \leqslant \dfrac{\pi}{2}$,

in the line $y = x$.

Warning: $\sin^{-1} x \neq \dfrac{1}{\sin x}$

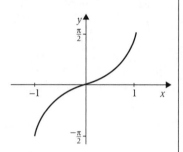

2 $\sin^{-1}(\sin x) = x$ for $-\dfrac{\pi}{2} \leqslant x \leqslant \dfrac{\pi}{2}$

$\sin(\sin^{-1} x) = x$ for $-1 \leqslant x \leqslant 1$

3 $\cos^{-1} x$ has domain $-1 \leqslant x \leqslant 1$ and range
$0 \leqslant \cos^{-1} x \leqslant \pi$.
The graph of $y = \cos^{-1} x$, $-1 \leqslant x \leqslant 1$ is obtained by
reflecting the graph of $y = \cos x$, $0 \leqslant x \leqslant \pi$
in the line $y = x$.

Warning: $\cos^{-1} x \neq \dfrac{1}{\cos x}$

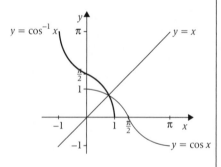

4 $\cos^{-1}(\cos x) = x$ for $0 \leqslant x \leqslant \pi$
$\cos(\cos^{-1} x) = x$ for $-1 \leqslant x \leqslant 1$

5 $\tan^{-1} x$ has domain all real numbers and

range $-\dfrac{\pi}{2} < \tan^{-1} x < \dfrac{\pi}{2}$.

The graph of $y = \tan^{-1} x$, is obtained by

reflecting the graph of $y = \tan x$,

$-\dfrac{\pi}{2} < x < \dfrac{\pi}{2}$,

in the line $y = x$.

Warning: $\tan^{-1} x \neq \dfrac{1}{\tan x}$

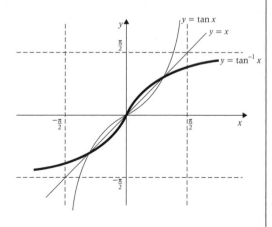

6 $\sec x = \dfrac{1}{\cos x}$

$\operatorname{cosec} x = \dfrac{1}{\sin x}$

$\cot x = \dfrac{1}{\tan x} = \dfrac{\cos x}{\sin x}$

3

7

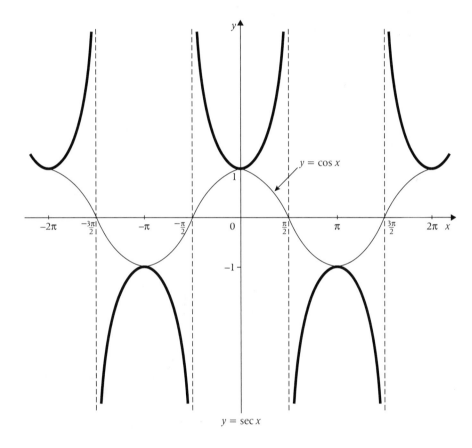

$y = \cos x$

$y = \sec x$

8

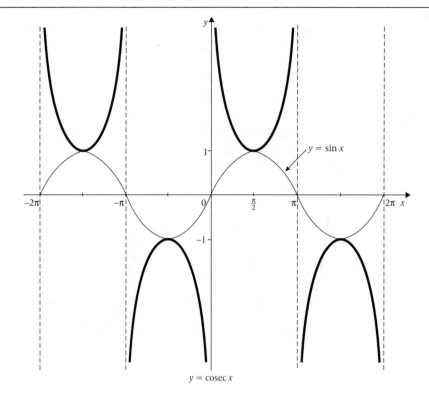

$y = \sin x$

$y = \operatorname{cosec} x$

9

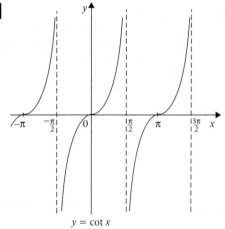

$y = \cot x$

$y = \cot x$

10 $1 + \tan^2 \theta \equiv \sec^2 \theta$

11 $\cot^2 \theta + 1 \equiv \operatorname{cosec}^2 \theta$

Worked example 1

A curve has equation $y = \tan^{-1} x$.

(a) Sketch the graph of the curve.

(b) The point $P(2, k)$ lies on the curve.

    (i) Find the value of k giving your answer to two decimal places.

    (ii) By drawing a suitable straight line on your sketch, show that the equation $2\tan^{-1} x - kx = 0$ has three roots and state their values.

3

(a)

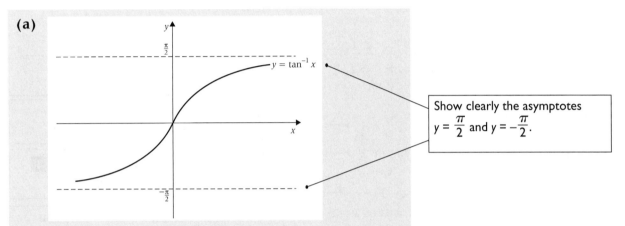

Show clearly the asymptotes $y = \dfrac{\pi}{2}$ and $y = -\dfrac{\pi}{2}$.

(b) (i) $(2, k)$ lies on the curve $y = \tan^{-1} x$

$$\Rightarrow k = \tan^{-1} 2$$
$$\Rightarrow k = 1.107\ldots = 1.11 \text{ (to 2dp)}$$

Set calculator to radian mode.

(ii) $2\tan^{-1} x - kx = 0 \Rightarrow \tan^{-1} x = \dfrac{k}{2}x$

The solutions of the equation $2\tan^{-1} x - kx = 0$ are the x-coordinates of the points of intersection of the curve $y = \tan^{-1} x$ and the line $y = \dfrac{k}{2}x$.

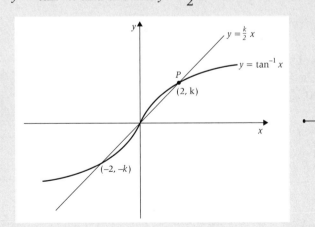

The line $y = \dfrac{k}{2}x$ passes through the origin and since $k = \dfrac{k}{2} \times 2$, $P(2, k)$ also lies on the line.

The three roots of $2\tan^{-1} x - kx = 0$ are $x = 0, -2$ and 2

Worked example 2

The curve C has equation $y = 2\cos^{-1}(x - 1)$

(a) Verify that the point $P(1, \pi)$ lies on C.

(b) Describe a sequence of geometrical transformations that maps the graph of $y = \cos^{-1} x$ onto the graph of $y = 2\cos^{-1}(x - 1)$

(c) The graph of C meets the x-axis at the point A and the y-axis at the point B. Find the equation of the line AB and verify that this line intersects C again at the point P.

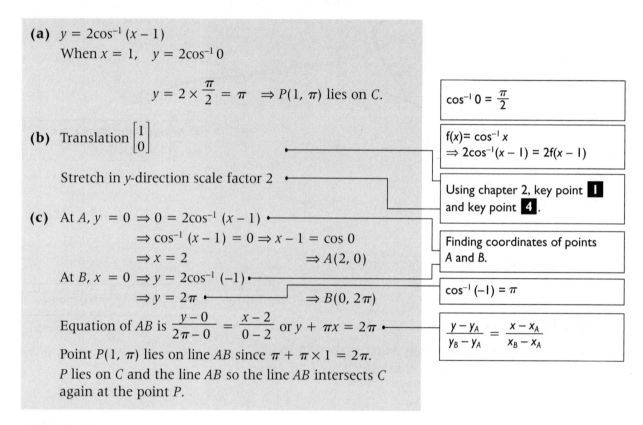

(a) $y = 2\cos^{-1}(x - 1)$

When $x = 1$, $y = 2\cos^{-1} 0$

$$y = 2 \times \frac{\pi}{2} = \pi \;\Rightarrow P(1, \pi) \text{ lies on } C.$$

> $\cos^{-1} 0 = \frac{\pi}{2}$

(b) Translation $\begin{bmatrix} 1 \\ 0 \end{bmatrix}$

> $f(x) = \cos^{-1} x$
> $\Rightarrow 2\cos^{-1}(x - 1) = 2f(x - 1)$

Stretch in y-direction scale factor 2

> Using chapter 2, key point **1** and key point **4**.

(c) At A, $y = 0 \Rightarrow 0 = 2\cos^{-1}(x - 1)$

$\Rightarrow \cos^{-1}(x - 1) = 0 \Rightarrow x - 1 = \cos 0$

$\Rightarrow x = 2 \qquad\qquad \Rightarrow A(2, 0)$

At B, $x = 0 \Rightarrow y = 2\cos^{-1}(-1)$

$\Rightarrow y = 2\pi \qquad\qquad \Rightarrow B(0, 2\pi)$

> Finding coordinates of points A and B.

> $\cos^{-1}(-1) = \pi$

Equation of AB is $\dfrac{y - 0}{2\pi - 0} = \dfrac{x - 2}{0 - 2}$ or $y + \pi x = 2\pi$

> $\dfrac{y - y_A}{y_B - y_A} = \dfrac{x - x_A}{x_B - x_A}$

Point $P(1, \pi)$ lies on line AB since $\pi + \pi \times 1 = 2\pi$.

P lies on C and the line AB so the line AB intersects C again at the point P.

Worked example 3

(a) Prove the identity $\cot A \sec A \operatorname{cosec} A - 1 \equiv \cot^2 A$.

(b) Solve the equation $\cot 2x \sec 2x \operatorname{cosec} 2x = 4$, giving all values of x in the interval $-90° < x < 90°$.

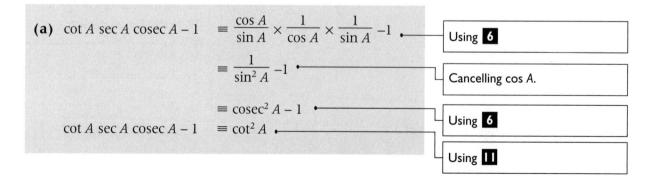

(a) $\cot A \sec A \operatorname{cosec} A - 1 \equiv \dfrac{\cos A}{\sin A} \times \dfrac{1}{\cos A} \times \dfrac{1}{\sin A} - 1$

> Using **6**

$\equiv \dfrac{1}{\sin^2 A} - 1$

> Cancelling cos A.

$\equiv \operatorname{cosec}^2 A - 1$

> Using **6**

$\cot A \sec A \operatorname{cosec} A - 1 \equiv \cot^2 A$

> Using **11**

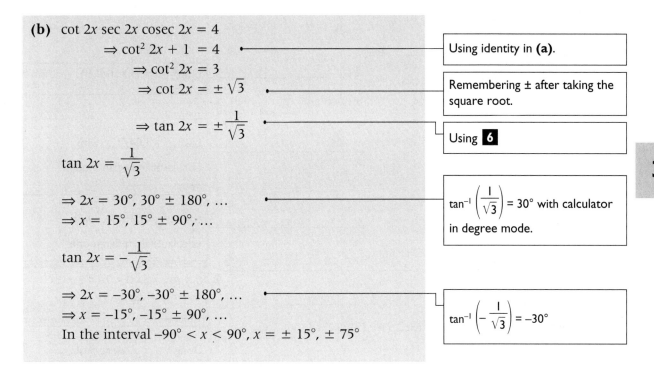

(b) $\cot 2x \sec 2x \operatorname{cosec} 2x = 4$

$\Rightarrow \cot^2 2x + 1 = 4$ — Using identity in **(a)**.

$\Rightarrow \cot^2 2x = 3$

$\Rightarrow \cot 2x = \pm \sqrt{3}$ — Remembering $\pm$ after taking the square root.

$\Rightarrow \tan 2x = \pm \dfrac{1}{\sqrt{3}}$ — Using **6**

$\tan 2x = \dfrac{1}{\sqrt{3}}$

$\Rightarrow 2x = 30°, 30° \pm 180°, \ldots$ — $\tan^{-1}\left(\dfrac{1}{\sqrt{3}}\right) = 30°$ with calculator in degree mode.

$\Rightarrow x = 15°, 15° \pm 90°, \ldots$

$\tan 2x = -\dfrac{1}{\sqrt{3}}$

$\Rightarrow 2x = -30°, -30° \pm 180°, \ldots$ — $\tan^{-1}\left(-\dfrac{1}{\sqrt{3}}\right) = -30°$

$\Rightarrow x = -15°, -15° \pm 90°, \ldots$

In the interval $-90° < x < 90°$, $x = \pm 15°, \pm 75°$

3

Worked example 4

It is given that $2\tan^2 x = \sec x + 4$

(a) Show that the equation $2\tan^2 x = \sec x + 4$ can be written in the form $2\sec^2 x - \sec x - 6 = 0$.

(b) Hence show that $\cos x = \dfrac{1}{2}$ or $\cos x = -\dfrac{2}{3}$.

(c) Hence solve the equation $2\tan^2 2\theta = \sec 2\theta + 4$ giving all values of θ in the interval $0 < \theta < \pi$ in radians to two decimal places.

(a) $2\tan^2 x \qquad = \sec x + 4$

$\Rightarrow 2(\sec^2 x - 1) \qquad = \sec x + 4$ — Using **10**

$\Rightarrow 2\sec^2 x - 2 \qquad = \sec x + 4$

$\Rightarrow 2\sec^2 x - \sec x - 6 \quad = 0$

(b) $2\sec^2 x - \sec x - 6 = 0 \Rightarrow (\sec x - 2)(2\sec x + 3) = 0$

$\Rightarrow \sec x = 2 \text{ or } \sec x \qquad = -\dfrac{3}{2}$

$\Rightarrow \cos x = \dfrac{1}{2} \text{ or } \cos x \qquad = -\dfrac{2}{3}$ — Using **6**, $\cos x = \dfrac{1}{\sec x}$

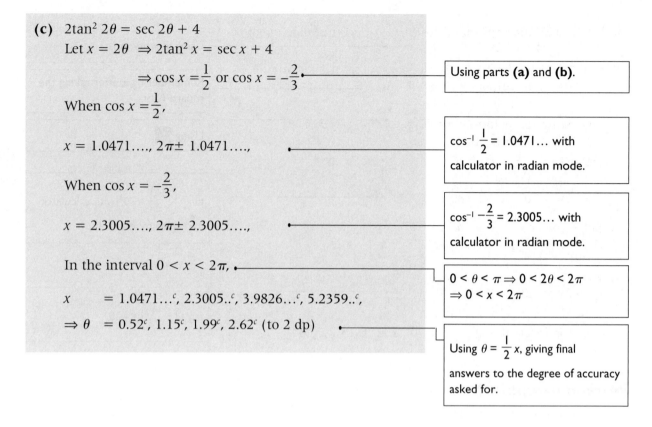

(c) $2\tan^2 2\theta = \sec 2\theta + 4$

Let $x = 2\theta \Rightarrow 2\tan^2 x = \sec x + 4$

$\Rightarrow \cos x = \dfrac{1}{2}$ or $\cos x = -\dfrac{2}{3}$. ———— Using parts **(a)** and **(b)**.

When $\cos x = \dfrac{1}{2}$,

$x = 1.0471...., 2\pi \pm 1.0471....,$ ———— $\cos^{-1}\dfrac{1}{2} = 1.0471...$ with calculator in radian mode.

When $\cos x = -\dfrac{2}{3}$,

$x = 2.3005...., 2\pi \pm 2.3005....,$ ———— $\cos^{-1}-\dfrac{2}{3} = 2.3005...$ with calculator in radian mode.

In the interval $0 < x < 2\pi$, ———— $0 < \theta < \pi \Rightarrow 0 < 2\theta < 2\pi$
$\Rightarrow 0 < x < 2\pi$

$x \quad = 1.0471...^c, 2.3005..^c, 3.9826...^c, 5.2359..^c,$

$\Rightarrow \theta = 0.52^c, 1.15^c, 1.99^c, 2.62^c \text{ (to 2 dp)}$ ———— Using $\theta = \dfrac{1}{2}x$, giving final answers to the degree of accuracy asked for.

REVISION EXERCISE 3

1 A curve has equation $y = 1 + \tan^{-1} x$.

   (a) The graph of $y = 1 + \tan^{-1} x$ intersects the x-axis at the point A and the y-axis at the point B. Show that the x-coordinate of A is -1.56 correct to three significant figures and find the coordinates of B.

   (b) Sketch the graph of $y = 1 + \tan^{-1} x$.

2 (a) Describe the geometrical transformation that maps the graph of $y = \sin^{-1} x$ onto the graph of $y = \sin^{-1}(x - 1)$.

   (b) The graph of $y = \sin^{-1}(x - 1)$ intersects the x-axis at the point A and the y-axis at the point B. Write down the coordinates of A and B.

   (c) (i) Sketch the graph of $y = \sin^{-1}(x - 1)$.

       (ii) By drawing a suitable straight line on your sketch, determine the number of real roots of the equation

$$\sin^{-1}(x - 1) = 1 - \frac{1}{2}x.$$

3 Find the exact values of

   (a) $\sin^{-1} 1$ **(b)** $\cos(\sin^{-1} 1)$ **(c)** $\cos\left(\cos^{-1}\dfrac{2}{3}\right)$ **(d)** $\sin\left(\cos^{-1}\dfrac{2}{3}\right)$

4 Given that θ is obtuse and $\sin \theta = \dfrac{3}{5}$, find the value of $\cot \theta$.

5 (a) Describe the sequence of geometrical transformations that maps the graph of $y = \operatorname{cosec} x$ onto the graph of $y = 1 + \operatorname{cosec} 2x$.

  (b) State the period, in radians, of the graph of $y = 1 + \operatorname{cosec} 2x$.

  (c) Sketch the graph of $y = 1 + \operatorname{cosec} 2x$ for

$$-\frac{\pi}{2} < x < \frac{\pi}{2}, x \neq 0.$$

6 Solve the equation $\operatorname{cosec}(x + 20°) = 2$, giving all solutions in the interval $-180° < x < 180°$.

7 Solve the equation $\cot 3x = -\sqrt{3}$, giving all solutions in the interval $0° < x < 180°$.

8 Solve the equation $\sec(2x - 30°) = 2$, giving all solutions in the interval $0° < x < 360°$.

9 (a) Sketch the graph of $y = |\sec x|$ for $-\pi \leq x \leq \pi, x \neq \pm \dfrac{\pi}{2}$.

  (b) Hence show that the equation $|\sec x| = 3$ has four solutions in the interval $-\pi \leq x \leq \pi$.

10 Solve the equation $\tan^2 x + \sec^2 x = 9$, giving all values of x to the nearest degree in the interval $0° < x < 360°$.

11 (a) Prove the identity
$2\sec^2 \theta - \tan \theta - 3 \equiv (2 \tan \theta + 1)(\tan \theta - 1)$.

  (b) Hence solve the equation $2\sec^2 \theta - \tan \theta - 3 = 0$, giving all values of θ in the interval $0 < \theta < 2\pi$, in radians to two decimal places.

12 (a) Solve the equation $\sec x = 3$, giving all solutions in the interval $0 < x < 2\pi$ to three significant figures.

  (b) Show that the equation $2\tan^2 x = \sec x + 13$ can be written in the form $(\sec x - 3)(2\sec x + 5) = 0$.

  (c) Solve the equation $2\tan^2 x = \sec x + 13$, giving all solutions in the interval $0 < x < 2\pi$ to three significant figures.

13 It is given that $2\operatorname{cosec}^2 x + \cot^2 x - 29 = 0$.

  (a) Show that the equation $2\operatorname{cosec}^2 x + \cot^2 x - 29 = 0$ can be written in the form $\cot^2 x - 9 = 0$.

  (b) Hence show that $\tan x = \dfrac{1}{3}$ or $\tan x = -\dfrac{1}{3}$.

(c) Hence solve the equation $2\cosec^2 2\theta + \cot^2 2\theta - 29 = 0$, giving all values of θ to the nearest degree in the interval $-90° < \theta < 90°$.

14 (a) Solve the equation $\cot x = -2$, giving all solutions in the interval $0 < x < 2\pi$ to three significant figures.

(b) Show that the equation $2\cosec^2 x = 8 - \cot x$ can be written in the form $(2\cot x - 3)(\cot x + 2) = 0$.

(c) Hence solve the equation $2\cosec^2 x = 8 - \cot x$, giving all solutions in the interval $0 < x < 2\pi$ to three significant figures.

15 It is given that $\cot^2 x = \cosec x + 11$.

(a) Show that the equation $\cot^2 x = \cosec x + 11$ can be written in the form $\cosec^2 x - \cosec x - 12 = 0$.

(b) Hence show that $\sin x = -\dfrac{1}{3}$ or $\sin x = \dfrac{1}{4}$.

(c) Hence solve the equation $\cot^2 x = \cosec x + 11$, giving all values of x, in the interval $0 < x < 2\pi$, to three significant figures.

16 Solve the equation $\tan^2(x + 80°) = \sec(x + 80°) + 1$, giving all values of x in the interval $0° \le x \le 360°$.

Test yourself	What to review
	If your answer is incorrect:
1 Find the exact values of **(a)** $\tan^{-1}\left(\tan\dfrac{\pi}{3}\right)$ **(b)** $\cos\left(\sin^{-1}\dfrac{2}{3}\right)$	Review Advancing Maths for AQA C3C4 pages 42–46.
2 By drawing a suitable line on the graph of $y = \sin^{-1} x$, determine the number of real roots of the equation $\sin^{-1} x + x = 1$.	Review Advancing Maths for AQA C3C4 pages 42–46.
3 Prove the identity $\dfrac{\cosec \theta + \sec \theta}{\tan \theta + \cot \theta} \equiv \cos \theta + \sin \theta$.	Review Advancing Maths for AQA C3C4 pages 46–50.
4 (a) Sketch the graph of $y = |\cot x|$ for $-\pi < x < \pi$, $x \ne 0$. **(b)** Hence determine the number of solutions of the equation $|\cot x| = 1$ that lie in the interval $-\pi < x < \pi$.	Review Advancing Maths for AQA C3C4 pages 50–53 and pg 31.

Test yourself (continued)

What to review

If your answer is incorrect:

5 **(a)** Solve the equation $\cot x = \dfrac{3}{2}$, giving all values of x to the nearest degree in the interval $0° < x < 360°$.

   (b) Show that the equation $2\operatorname{cosec}^2 x + 5\cot x - 14 = 0$ can be written in the form $2\cot^2 x + 5\cot x - 12 = 0$.

   (c) Hence solve the equation $2\operatorname{cosec}^2 x + 5\cot x - 14 = 0$ giving all values of x to the nearest degree in the interval $0° < x < 360°$.

Review Advancing Maths for AQA C3C4 pages 53–56.

6 **(a)** Show that the equation $3\tan^2 x = 8\sec x + 13$ can be written in the form $3\sec^2 x - 8\sec x - 16 = 0$.

   (b) Hence show that $\cos x = -\dfrac{3}{4}$ or $\cos x = \dfrac{1}{4}$.

   (c) Hence solve the equation $3\tan^2 x = 8\sec x + 13$, giving all solutions in the interval $-\pi \le x \le \pi$ to three significant figures.

Review Advancing Maths for AQA C3C4 pages 53–56.

3

Test yourself ANSWERS

6 (c) $\pm 1.32^c,\ \pm 2.42^c$

5 (a) $34°,\ 214°$; **(c)** $34°,\ 166°,\ 214°,\ 346°$.

4 (b) 4

4 (a)

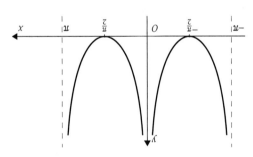

2 1

1 (a) $\dfrac{\pi}{3}$ **(b)** $\dfrac{\sqrt{5}}{3}$

CHAPTER 4

The number e and calculus

Key points to remember

1 The number e is irrational and its value is approximately 2.718.

2 The curve with equation $y = e^x$ has derivative $\frac{dy}{dx} = e^x$.

3 $\frac{d}{dx}(e^{kx}) = ke^{kx}$.

4 $\int e^{kx}\, dx = \frac{1}{k}e^{kx} + \text{constant}$.

5 The natural logarithm $\ln x$ is defined for $x > 0$.
A useful equivalent statement is

$$x = e^y \Leftrightarrow y = \ln x.$$

6 The derivative of $\ln x$ is $\frac{1}{x}$.

7 $\int \frac{1}{x}\, dx = \ln x + \text{constant}$.

Worked example 1

Solve the equations

(a) $e^{3x} = 27$;

(b) $e^x + 2e^{-x} = 3$.

(a) $e^{3x} = 27 \;\Rightarrow\; 3x = \ln 27$ ⸻ Using **5**

$\Rightarrow 3x = 3\ln 3$ ⸻ Using laws of logs.

$\Rightarrow x = \ln 3$

You could have taken cube roots of both sides instead, giving

$$e^x = 3 \;\Rightarrow\; x = \ln 3.$$ ⸻ Using **5**

(b) You need to multiply both sides by e^x

$$e^{2x} + 2 = 3e^x$$ ⸻ Since $e^x \times e^x = e^{2x}$ and $e^x \times e^{-x} = 1$.

$$\Rightarrow e^{2x} - 3e^x + 2 = 0.$$

Writing $y = e^x$ gives $y^2 - 3y + 2 = 0$

Factorising gives

$(y - 1)(y - 2) = 0$

$\Rightarrow y = 1$ or $y = 2$

$\Rightarrow e^x = 1$ or $e^x = 2$

$\Rightarrow x = \ln 1$ or $x = \ln 2$

Hence $x = 0$ or $x = \ln 2$

> You may feel confident enough to write $(e^x - 1)(e^x - 2) = 0$ without introducing y.

> Simplify using $\ln 1 = 0$.

Worked example 2

A curve has equation $y = \dfrac{e^{5x} + 3}{e^{2x}}$.

(a) **(i)** Find the x-coordinate of the stationary point, M, of the curve.

   (ii) Determine the nature of this stationary point, M.

(b) Find an equation of the tangent at the point on the curve where $x = 0$.

(a) **(i)** $y = \dfrac{e^{5x} + 3}{e^{2x}}$ can be written as $y = e^{3x} + 3e^{-2x}$

Hence $\dfrac{dy}{dx} = 3e^{3x} - 6e^{-2x}$

> Using **3**

Stationary point occurs when $\dfrac{dy}{dx} = 0$.

$\Rightarrow 3e^{3x} - 6e^{-2x} = 0$.

$\Rightarrow e^{5x} = 2$

$\Rightarrow 5x = \ln 2$

> Multiply both sides by e^{2x}.

Hence the x-coordinate of the stationary point is $\dfrac{1}{5}\ln 2$.

   (ii) $\dfrac{d^2 y}{dx^2} = 9e^{3x} + 12e^{-2x}$

when $x = \dfrac{1}{5}\ln 2$, $\dfrac{d^2 y}{dx^2} > 0$

Hence M is a minimum point.

> The second derivative test is a quick way to determine whether it is a maximum or minimum point.

(b) Substituting $x = 0$ into $\dfrac{dy}{dx} = 3e^{3x} - 6e^{-2x}$

gives $\dfrac{dy}{dx} = 3 - 6 = -3$.

Substituting $x = 0$ into $y = \dfrac{e^{5x} + 3}{e^{2x}}$ gives $y = 4$.

The tangent has gradient -3 and passes through $(0,4)$

The tangent has equation $y = -3x + 4$ or $3x + y = 4$.

> Any correct form would score full marks.

Worked example 3

The diagram shows a sketch of the curve $y = e^{3x} - 4$. The curve crosses the y-axis at A and the x-axis at B.

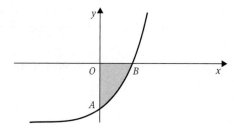

(a) Find the coordinates of A and B.

(b) (i) Sketch the graph of $y = |e^{3x} - 4|$.
    (ii) Solve the equation $|e^{3x} - 4| = 1$.

(c) Find a sequence of geometrical transformations which maps the graph of $y = e^x$ onto the graph of $y = e^{3x} - 4$.

(d) Find the area of the shaded region bounded by the curve and the coordinate axes.

(a) When $x = 0$, $y = 1 - 4 = -3$
Hence A has coordinates $(0, -3)$.
Putting $y = 0$ gives $e^{3x} - 4 = 0$
Hence $e^{3x} = 4 \Rightarrow 3x = \ln 4 \Rightarrow x = \frac{1}{3}\ln 4$
Coordinates of B are $\left(\frac{1}{3}\ln 4, 0\right)$

(b) (i)

It is as if the part of the graph that was below the x-axis has been reflected in the x-axis.

(ii) The line $y = 1$ cuts the graph above at two points.
Solving $e^{3x} - 4 = 1 \Rightarrow e^{3x} = 5$.
$\Rightarrow 3x = \ln 5 \Rightarrow x = \frac{1}{3}\ln 5$.

Solving $e^{3x} - 4 = -1 \Rightarrow e^{3x} = 3$.
$\Rightarrow 3x = \ln 3 \Rightarrow x = \frac{1}{3}\ln 3$.

The two solutions are $\frac{1}{3}\ln 3$ and $\frac{1}{3}\ln 5$.

(c) The graph of $y = e^x$ is stretched by scale factor $\frac{1}{3}$ in the x-direction and translated through $\begin{bmatrix} 0 \\ -4 \end{bmatrix}$ in order to produce the graph of $y = e^{3x} - 4$.

(d) The value of x at B is $\frac{1}{3} \ln 4$.

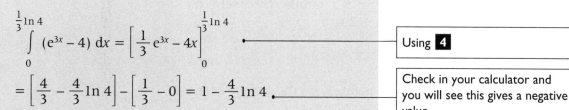

$$\int_0^{\frac{1}{3}\ln 4} (e^{3x} - 4)\, dx = \left[\frac{1}{3} e^{3x} - 4x \right]_0^{\frac{1}{3}\ln 4}$$

Using **4**

$$= \left[\frac{4}{3} - \frac{4}{3}\ln 4 \right] - \left[\frac{1}{3} - 0 \right] = 1 - \frac{4}{3}\ln 4$$

Check in your calculator and you will see this gives a negative value.

4

The region is entirely below the x-axis.
To find the given area, the value of the integral must be multiplied by -1.

The area of the shaded region is $\left(\frac{4}{3}\ln 4 \right) - 1$

Worked example 4

A curve is defined for $x > 0$ by the equation
$$y = 3x^2 - 14x + 8\ln x + 5.$$

(a) Show that the x-coordinates of the stationary points satisfy the equation
$$3x^2 - 7x + 4 = 0.$$

(b) Hence find the x-coordinates of the stationary points of the curve.

(a) $y = 3x^2 - 14x + 8\ln x + 5$

$\Rightarrow \dfrac{dy}{dx} = 6x - 14 + \dfrac{8}{x}$

Using **6**

Stationary points occur when $\dfrac{dy}{dx} = 0$

Hence $6x^2 - 14x + 8 = 0$

Multiplying both sides by x.

Therefore $3x^2 - 7x + 4 = 0$

Dividing both sides by 2.

(b) Factorising gives $(x - 1)(3x - 4) = 0$
Stationary points occur when $x = 1$ or $x = \dfrac{4}{3}$

REVISION EXERCISE 4

1 (a) Solve the equation $e^{2x} = 25$.

(b) Using the substitution $y = e^x$, or otherwise, solve the equation $2e^x + 3e^{-x} = 7$.

2 (a) Solve the equation $\ln 3x = 6$.

(b) Using the substitution $y = \ln x$, or otherwise, solve the equation $(\ln x)^2 - 3\ln x + 2 = 0$.

3 A curve has equation $y = \dfrac{e^{7x} - 4}{e^{3x}}$.

(a) Find the gradient at the point, P, on the curve where $x = 0$.

(b) Hence find an equation of the tangent at P.

4 Show that the curve with equation $y = e^{3x} - 3x + 5$ has a stationary point at $S(0, 6)$.

Find the value of $\dfrac{d^2 y}{dx^2}$ when $x = 0$ and hence determine the nature of the stationary point at S.

5 A curve is defined for $x \geqslant 0$ by the equation $y = e^{5x} - x\sqrt{x} + 3$ and the point A on the curve has x-coordinate equal to 0.

(a) Find the gradient of the curve at the point A.

(b) Find an equation of the normal to the curve at A.

6 Find **(a)** $\displaystyle\int_0^1 e^{-3x}dx$ **(b)** $\displaystyle\int_0^{\ln 2} (1 + 3e^x)^2 \, dx$ **(c)** $\displaystyle\int_0^3 \dfrac{3e^{5x} + 4}{e^{2x}} \, dx$.

7 A curve has equation $y = e^{2x} - 4x + 7$.

(a) Find the coordinates of the stationary point of the curve and determine its nature.

(b) Find the area of the region bounded by the curve, the line $x = -1$ and the y-axis.

8 A curve has equation $y = 6 - x - 3e^{-x}$.

(a) Find $\dfrac{dy}{dx}$ and $\dfrac{d^2y}{dx^2}$.

(b) Find the coordinates of the stationary point of the curve and determine its nature.

9 (a) Sketch the graph of $y = e^{-3x} + 2$.

(b) Find the equation of the normal to the curve
$y = e^{-3x} + 2$ at the point $(0, 3)$, and find the coordinates
of the point where this normal crosses the x-axis.

(c) Find the area of the region bounded by the curve with
equation $y = e^{-3x} + 2$, the coordinate axes and the line
$x = 1$.

10 A curve has equation $y = 1 - \ln 2x$.

(a) Find the value of x at the point where the curve crosses
the x-axis.

(b) (i) Find the gradient of the curve at the point $P\left(\frac{1}{2}, 1\right)$.

(ii) Hence find an equation of the tangent to
the curve at P.

11 The function f is defined for all real positive values of x by
$$f(x) = e^{-3x} + \frac{2}{x} - 3.$$

(a) Prove that f is a decreasing function.

(b) Find the range of f .

(c) Find $\displaystyle\int_{1}^{2} f(x)\, dx$.

12 The curve with equation $y = 5 - e^{\frac{x}{2}}$ and the tangent to the
curve at the point P, where the curve crosses the y-axis, are
sketched below.

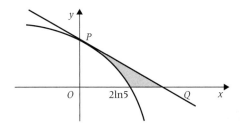

(a) State the coordinates of the point P.

(b) (i) Find an equation of the tangent to the curve at P.

(ii) Hence find the coordinates of Q, where this
tangent crosses the x-axis.

(c) (i) Find $\displaystyle\int \left(5 - e^{\frac{x}{2}}\right) dx$.

(ii) Find the area of the shaded region bounded by the
curve, the x-axis and the tangent to the curve at P.

4

13 The curve with equation $y = 9e^{2x} - 16$ is sketched below.

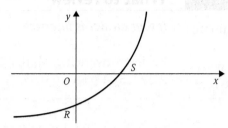

(a) (i) State the coordinates of R, where the curve crosses the y-axis.

(ii) Show that the x-coordinate of the point S, where the curve crosses the x-axis is $2\ln 2 - \ln 3$.

(b) (i) Sketch the graph of $y = |9e^{2x} - 16|$.

(ii) Solve the equation $|9e^{2x} - 16| = 7$.

(c) Find the area of the region ORS, bounded by the curve $y = 9e^{2x} - 16$ and the coordinate axes.

14 (a) The function f is defined for all real values of x by
$f(x) = 3e^{4x} + 2$.

(i) Find the range of f.

(ii) Find an expression for $f^{-1}(x)$, where f^{-1} is the inverse of f.

(b) A curve has equation $y = 3e^{4x} + 2$.

(i) Find an equation of the normal to the curve at the point where $x = 0$.

(ii) Find the area bounded by the curve, the coordinate axes and the line $x = \dfrac{1}{4}$.

15 A curve is defined for $x > 0$ by the equation
$y = x^2 - 5x + 3\ln x + 7$

(a) Show that the x-coordinates of the stationary points satisfy the equation
$$2x^2 - 5x + 3 = 0$$

(b) Hence find the coordinates of the stationary points of the curve.

Test yourself	What to review
	If your answer is incorrect:

1 Find the gradient of the curve with equation
$y = 3e^{2x} - e^{-3x}$ at the point where $x = 0$.

Review Advancing Maths for
AQA C3C4 pages 63–65.

2 Find **(a)** $\displaystyle\int_{0}^{1} e^{4x}\,dx$ **(b)** $\displaystyle\int_{-1}^{0}(3 + e^{-x})^2\,dx$.

Review Advancing Maths for
AQA C3C4 pages 65–66.

3 A curve has equation $y = 2 + 6x + e^{-3x}$.
  (a) Find the coordinates of the stationary point of the curve
and determine its nature.
  (b) Find the area of the finite region bounded by the curve,
the coordinate axes and the line $x = 1$.

Review Advancing Maths for
AQA C3C4 pages 68–70.

4

4 Find $\displaystyle\int_{1}^{2}\dfrac{x^3 - 6}{x^4}\,dx$.

Review Advancing Maths for
AQA C3C4 page 71.

5 Solve the equation $3e^{2x} - 7e^x + 2 = 0$.

Review Advancing Maths for
AQA C3C4 pages 74–75.

Test yourself ANSWERS

4 $\ln 2 - \dfrac{7}{4}$ **5** $x = -\ln 3,\ x = \ln 2$

3 **(a)** $\left(-\dfrac{1}{3}\ln 2,\ 4 - 2\ln 2\right)$; Minimum point **(b)** $\dfrac{16}{3} - \dfrac{1}{3}e^{-3}$

2 **(a)** $\dfrac{1}{4}(e^4 - 1)$ **(b)** $2.5 + 6e + \dfrac{1}{2}e^2$

1 9

CHAPTER 5

Further differentiation and the chain rule

Key points to remember

1 $\dfrac{d}{dx}(\sin x) = \cos x$, where x is in radians.

2 $\dfrac{d}{dx}(\cos x) = -\sin x$, where x is in radians.

3 The chain rule can be used to differentiate composite functions. The chain rule is

$$\dfrac{dy}{dx} = \dfrac{dy}{du} \times \dfrac{du}{dx} \quad \text{or in function notation}$$

$$\dfrac{dy}{dx} = g'(u) \times f'(x) \quad \text{where } y = gf(x) \text{ and } u = f(x).$$

4 The chain rule can be extended to

$$\dfrac{dy}{dx} = \dfrac{dy}{dv} \times \dfrac{dv}{du} \times \dfrac{du}{dx}.$$

5 $\dfrac{dy}{dx} = \dfrac{1}{\dfrac{dx}{dy}} \quad \text{or} \quad \dfrac{dx}{dy} = \dfrac{1}{\dfrac{dy}{dx}}$

Worked example 1

The curve $y = 8\sin x + 2x - 3$ is defined for $0 \leqslant x \leqslant 2\pi$.

(a) Find the x-coordinates of the stationary points of the curve, giving your answers to 3 significant figures.

(b) Find $\dfrac{d^2y}{dx^2}$ and hence determine the nature of the stationary points.

(a) $y = 8\sin x + 2x - 3 \Rightarrow \dfrac{dy}{dx} = 8\cos x + 2$ ←————————— Using **1**

Stationary points occur when $\dfrac{dy}{dx} = 0$

Hence $8\cos x + 2 = 0 \Rightarrow \cos x = -\dfrac{1}{4}$

In the interval $0 < x < 2\pi$

$x = 1.823\dots$ or $x = 2\pi - 1.823\dots \approx 4.460$

The x-coordinates of the stationary points are 1.82 and 4.46 (to 3 significant figures).

(b) Since $\dfrac{dy}{dx} = 8\cos x + 2$,

$\dfrac{d^2y}{dx^2} = -8\sin x$ ←————————— Using **2**

When $x = 1.82$, $\dfrac{d^2y}{dx^2} \approx -7.75 < 0$

Hence, the stationary point where $x = 1.82$ is a maximum point.

When $x = 4.46$, $\dfrac{d^2y}{dx^2} \approx 7.75 > 0$

Hence, the stationary point where $x = 4.46$ is a minimum point.

5

Worked example 2

A curve has equation $y = 3\cos x + 2e^x$. Find the equation of the normal to the curve at the point $(0, 5)$.

$y = 3\cos x + 2e^x \Rightarrow \dfrac{dy}{dx} = -3\sin x + 2e^x$ ←————————— Using **2**

When $x = 0$, $\Rightarrow \dfrac{dy}{dx} = -3\sin 0 + 2e^0 = 0 + 2 = 2$

Gradient of normal $= -\dfrac{1}{2}$.

Normal has equation $y - 5 = -\dfrac{1}{2}(x - 0)$

or $x + 2y = 10$

Worked example 3

Differentiate each of the following with respect to x:

(a) $(3x^2 + 5)^7$ **(b)** $\sin(6x - 7)$ **(c)** $\ln(x^3 + 4x - 8)$

(a) Write $y = (3x^2 + 5)^7$

Let $u = 3x^2 + 5$, then $y = u^7$

$$\frac{du}{dx} = 6x \text{ and } \frac{dy}{du} = 7u^6$$

$$\frac{dy}{dx} = \frac{dy}{du} \times \frac{du}{dx}$$

Using **3**

$$\frac{du}{dx} = (7u^6)\, 6x = 42xu^6 = 42x(3x^2 + 5)^6$$

(b) Write $y = \sin(6x - 7)$

Let $u = 6x - 7$, then $y = \sin u$

$$\frac{du}{dx} = 6 \text{ and } \frac{dy}{du} = \cos u$$

Using **1**

$$\frac{dy}{dx} = \frac{dy}{du} \times \frac{du}{dx}$$

Using **3**

$$\frac{dy}{dx} = (\cos u) \times 6 = 6\cos(6x - 7)$$

(c) $y = \ln(x^3 + 4x - 8)$

Writing $u = x^3 + 4x - 8$ gives $y = \ln u$

$$\frac{du}{dx} = 3x^2 + 4 \text{ and } \frac{dy}{du} = \frac{1}{u}$$

$$\frac{dy}{dx} = \frac{dy}{du} \times \frac{du}{dx}$$

Using **3**

$$\frac{dy}{dx} = \left(\frac{1}{u}\right)(3x^2 + 4) = \frac{3x^2 + 4}{x^3 + 4x - 8}$$

Worked example 4

Find $\dfrac{dy}{dx}$ for each of the following:

(a) $y = (3 + \cos 4x)^6$ **(b)** $y = \sin^3 (4 + \ln x)$

(a) $y = (3 + \cos 4x)^6$

Let $u = (3 + \cos 4x)$, then $y = u^6$

$\dfrac{du}{dx} = -4\sin 4x; \dfrac{dy}{du} = 6u^5$

> Hopefully you can differentiate cos 4x in your head using the chain rule, without needing to write down a substitution.

$\dfrac{du}{dx} = \dfrac{dy}{du} \times \dfrac{du}{dx}$

> Using **3**

$\dfrac{dy}{dx} = 6u^5 \times (-4\sin 4x) = -24\sin 4x \,(3 + \cos 4x)^5$

(b) $y = \sin^3 (4 + \ln x)$

Let $u = (4 + \ln x)$, $v = \sin u$, then $y = v^3$

$\dfrac{du}{dx} = \dfrac{1}{x}; \dfrac{dv}{du} = \cos u; \dfrac{dy}{dv} = 3v^2$

$\dfrac{dy}{dx} = \dfrac{dy}{dv} \times \dfrac{dv}{du} \times \dfrac{du}{dx}$

> Using **4**

$\dfrac{dy}{dx} = 3v^2 \times \cos u \times \dfrac{1}{x} = \dfrac{3v^2}{x} \cos u = \dfrac{3}{x} \sin^2 u \cos u$

$\Rightarrow \dfrac{dy}{dx} = \dfrac{3}{x} \sin^2 (4 + \ln x) \cos (4 + \ln x)$

Worked example 5

(a) Differentiate $\sqrt{x^2 + 3}$ with respect to x.

(b) Find the x-coordinates of the stationary points of the curve with equation $y = x^2 - 4\sqrt{x^2 + 3}$.

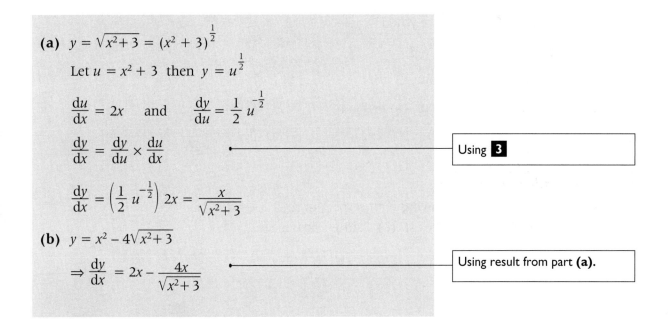

(a) $y = \sqrt{x^2 + 3} = (x^2 + 3)^{\frac{1}{2}}$

Let $u = x^2 + 3$ then $y = u^{\frac{1}{2}}$

$\dfrac{du}{dx} = 2x$ and $\dfrac{dy}{du} = \dfrac{1}{2} u^{-\frac{1}{2}}$

$\dfrac{dy}{dx} = \dfrac{dy}{du} \times \dfrac{du}{dx}$

> Using **3**

$\dfrac{dy}{dx} = \left(\dfrac{1}{2} u^{-\frac{1}{2}}\right) 2x = \dfrac{x}{\sqrt{x^2 + 3}}$

(b) $y = x^2 - 4\sqrt{x^2 + 3}$

> Using result from part **(a)**.

$\Rightarrow \dfrac{dy}{dx} = 2x - \dfrac{4x}{\sqrt{x^2 + 3}}$

5

Stationary points occur when $\dfrac{dy}{dx} = 0$

$2x - \dfrac{4x}{\sqrt{x^2+3}} = 0 \Rightarrow 2x\left(1 - \dfrac{2}{\sqrt{x^2+3}}\right) = 0$

either $x = 0$ or $\sqrt{x^2+3} = 2 \Rightarrow x^2 + 3 = 4$

$\Rightarrow x^2 = 1 \Rightarrow x = \pm 1$

Stationary points occur when $x = 0$, $x = -1$ and $x = 1$.

Worked example 6

A curve has equation $x = y^2 + 3 + 4\sin y$.

(a) Find $\dfrac{dx}{dy}$ in terms of y.

(b) Hence find $\dfrac{dy}{dx}$ in terms of y.

(c) Find the equation of the tangent to the curve at the point on the curve where $y = 0$.

(a) $x = y^2 + 3 + 4\sin y \Rightarrow \dfrac{dx}{dy} = 2y + 4\cos y$ Using **1**

(b) $\dfrac{dy}{dx} = \dfrac{1}{2y + 4\cos y}$ Using **5**

(c) When $y = 0$, $\dfrac{dy}{dx} = \dfrac{1}{0 + 4} = \dfrac{1}{4}$.

Tangent has gradient $\dfrac{1}{4}$ and since when

$y = 0$, $x = 0 + 3 + 4\sin 0 = 3$,

The curve passes through the point $(3, 0)$.

The tangent has equation $y = \dfrac{1}{4}(x - 3)$ or $x - 4y = 3$.

REVISION EXERCISE 5

1 Differentiate each of the following with respect to x:
   (a) $x^2 + 4\sin x$; **(b)** $e^x + 5\cos x$; **(c)** $2\sin x - 3\cos x$.

2 A curve has equation $y = 4\sin x + 5\cos x - 3$.

   (a) Find $\dfrac{dy}{dx}$.

   (b) The point P on the curve is where $x = 0$. Find an equation of the tangent to the curve at the point P.

   (c) Show that the stationary points of the curve occur when $\tan x = 0.8$.

3 The function f is defined for all real values of x by
$$f(x) = 5\cos x - 7x + 3.$$

   (a) (i) Find the derivative $f'(x)$.

   (ii) Find the range of f'.

   (b) Prove that f is a decreasing function.

4 Differentiate each of the following with respect to x:

   (a) $(3x + 4)^5$ **(b)** $(x^2 + 7)^6$ **(c)** $(4x + 5)^{\frac{1}{2}}$

   (d) $(5x^2 + 2x - 3)^4$ **(e)** $\ln(3x + 7)$ **(f)** $(x^2 + 2x + 5)^{\frac{3}{2}}$

   (g) $2e^{3x} - 3(x + 1)^4$ **(h)** $\sqrt{1 + x^2}$

5 Find $\dfrac{dy}{dx}$ for each of the following:

   (a) $y = 6\cos 2x$ **(b)** $y = 7\sin 6x$ **(c)** $y = 7\sin 3x + 3\cos 5x$
   (d) $y = e^{4x-5}$ **(e)** $y = e^{\sin x}$ **(f)** $y = \ln(2 - \cos x)$

6 A curve has equation $y = x - 5 - 4\sqrt{x + 3}$ and is defined for $x > -3$.

   (a) Find $\dfrac{dy}{dx}$.

   (b) Hence find the coordinates of the stationary point of the curve.

7 A curve has equation $y = 6(x^2 + 5)^{\frac{1}{2}} - x^2$.

   (a) Find $\dfrac{dy}{dx}$.

   (b) Hence find the coordinates of the stationary points of the curve.

8 A curve has equation $y = (x^3 - 2x + 2)^7$.

   (a) Find the value of $\dfrac{dy}{dx}$ when $x = 1$.

   (b) Hence find an equation of the normal to the curve at the point $(1, 1)$.

9 By first finding $\dfrac{dx}{dy}$, find $\dfrac{dy}{dx}$, in terms of y, for each of the following curves:

    (a) $x = y^3 + 3y^2 - 2$ **(b)** $x = 4\sin(y - 3)$
    (c) $x = 3\cos(y^2 + 1)$

10 A curve, defined for $y > 0$, has equation
    $x = y^2 + 4 + 3\ln y + \sin(y - 1)$

    (a) Verify that the point $(5, 1)$ lies on the curve.

    (b) Find $\dfrac{dx}{dy}$.

    (c) Hence find an equation of the tangent to the curve at the point $(5, 1)$.

Test yourself	What to review
	If your answer is incorrect:
1 Find an equation of the tangent to the curve $y = 4x^3 + 1 + 2\sin x$ at the point $P(0, 1)$.	Review Advancing Maths for AQA C3C4 pages 82–85.

2   The function f is defined for all real values of x by
         $f(x) = 4\cos x + 5x - 2$.
 	
    (a) (i)   Find the derivative $f'(x)$.
        (ii)   Find the range of f'.
    (b)   Prove that f is an increasing function.
	Review Advancing Maths for AQA C3C4 pages 82–85.

3   Differentiate the following with respect to x:
 	
    (a) $y = (3x^2 + x - 2)^8$ **(b)** $y = 3\sin 4x$
    (c) $y = 5e^{6x} + 2(x - 1)^5$ **(d)** $\sqrt[3]{3x - 5}$
	Review Advancing Maths for AQA C3C4 pages 86–89.

4   Find $\dfrac{dy}{dx}$ when:
 	
    (a) $y = \cos^3 2x$ **(b)** $y = (2 + e^{3x})^5$
    (c) $y = \ln(\sin 5x)$
	Review Advancing Maths for AQA C3C4 pages 90–91.

5   A curve, defined for $y > 0$, has equation
         $x = 6\ln y + (y - 2)^4$
 	
    (a)   Find $\dfrac{dx}{dy}$.
    (b)   Hence find the gradient at the point on the curve where $y = 3$.
	Review Advancing Maths for AQA C3C4 pages 92–95.

Test yourself ANSWERS

1 $y = 2x + 1$

2 (a) (i) $5 - 4\sin x$ **(ii)** $1 \leqslant f'(x) \leqslant 9$

(b) $f'(x) > 0$ for all values of x. Hence f is an increasing function.

3 (a) $8(6x + 1)(3x^2 + x - 2)^7$ **(b)** $12\cos 4x$ **(c)** $y = 30e^{6x} + 10(x - 1)^4$

(d) $(3x - 5)^{-\frac{2}{3}}$

4 (a) $-6\cos^2 2x \sin 2x$ **(b)** $15e^{3x}(2 + e^{3x})^4$ **(c)** $\dfrac{5\cos 5x}{\sin 5x}$

5 (a) $\dfrac{6}{y} + 4(y - 2)^3$ **(b)** $\dfrac{1}{6}$

5

CHAPTER 6

Differentiation using the product and the quotient rule

Key points to remember

1 To differentiate a product $y = u \times v$, you can use the **product rule**:

$$\frac{dy}{dx} = u\frac{dv}{dx} + v\frac{du}{dx}$$

2 Using function notation, the derivative of the product $f(x)g(x)$ is
$$f(x)g'(x) + f'(x)g(x)$$

3 To differentiate a quotient $y = \dfrac{u}{v}$, you can use the **quotient rule**:

$$\frac{dy}{dx} = \frac{v\dfrac{du}{dx} - u\dfrac{dv}{dx}}{v^2}$$

4 Using function notation, the derivative of the quotient $\dfrac{f(x)}{g(x)}$ is
$$\frac{f'(x)g(x) - f(x)g'(x)}{[g(x)]^2}$$

This formula is given in the formulae booklet for use in the examination.

5 $\dfrac{d}{dx}(\tan x) = \sec^2 x$

$\dfrac{d}{dx}(\cot x) = -\mathrm{cosec}^2 x$

$\dfrac{d}{dx}(\sec x) = \sec x \tan x$

$\dfrac{d}{dx}(\mathrm{cosec}\, x) = -\mathrm{cosec}\, x \cot x$

These formulae are given in the formulae booklet for use in the examination.

Worked example 1

Differentiate with respect to x:

(a) $x^2 \ln x$ **(b)** $e^{2x} \cos x$ **(c)** $(x^3 - 7x)\sin 3x$

> Each of these parts involves the product rule and three different approaches are demonstrated in the solution.

(a) Let $y = x^2 \ln x$ so that $y = u \times v$

> This is a product and so the product rule must be used.

Writing $u = x^2$ and $v = \ln x$

$$\frac{du}{dx} = 2x \quad \text{and} \quad \frac{dv}{dx} = \frac{1}{x}$$

> This formula needs to be learnt.

Then $\quad \dfrac{dy}{dx} = u\dfrac{dv}{dx} + v\dfrac{du}{dx}$

> Using **1**

$$\frac{dy}{dx} = (x^2)\left(\frac{1}{x}\right) + (\ln x)(2x) = x + 2x \ln x$$

(b) Regarding $e^{2x} \cos x$ as $f(x)g(x)$.

> This is another product.

$$f(x) = e^{2x} \quad \Rightarrow f'(x) = 2e^{2x}$$
$$g(x) = \cos x \quad \Rightarrow g'(x) = -\sin x$$

The derivative is given by

$$f(x)g'(x) + f'(x)g(x)$$

> Using **2**

$$= (e^{2x})(-\sin x) + (2e^{2x})(\cos x)$$
$$= e^{2x}(2 \cos x - \sin x)$$

> Taking out a common factor.

(c) Let $y = (x^3 - 7x)\sin 3x$

$$\frac{dy}{dx} = (x^3 - 7x)(3\cos 3x) + (\sin 3x)(3x^2 - 7)$$

$$= 3(x^3 - 7x) \cos 3x + (3x^2 - 7)\sin 3x$$

> The product rule is essentially (first term) (derivative of second term) + (second term) (derivative of first term).

6

Worked example 2

A curve has equation $y = x^2 e^{-3x}$. Find the coordinates of the stationary points of the curve.

$$y = x^2 e^{-3x} \Rightarrow \frac{dy}{dx} = x^2(-3e^{-3x}) + (2x)e^{-3x}$$

$$\Rightarrow \frac{dy}{dx} = e^{-3x}(2x - 3x^2)$$

Stationary points occur when $\dfrac{dy}{dx} = 0$

Since $e^{-3x} > 0$ for all values of x,
$$\Rightarrow 2x - 3x^2 = x(2 - 3x) = 0$$
$$\Rightarrow x = 0 \text{ or } x = \frac{2}{3}$$

When $x = 0$, $y = 0$.
One stationary point has coordinates $(0, 0)$.

When $x = \frac{2}{3}$, $y = \left(\frac{2}{3}\right)^2 e^{-2} = \frac{4}{9}e^{-2}$.

Second stationary point is $\left(\frac{2}{3}, \frac{4}{9}e^{-2}\right)$.

Worked example 3

Find $\dfrac{dy}{dx}$ for each of the following:

(a) $y = \dfrac{2 - 3x}{x + 4}$ **(b)** $y = \dfrac{\sin 3x}{x^2 + 1}$ **(c)** $y = \dfrac{e^{4x}}{2 + \cos 5x}$

(a) $y = \dfrac{2 - 3x}{x + 4} = \dfrac{f(x)}{g(x)}$

> This suggests the quotient rule and you can use the formula given in the formulae booklet.

$$\frac{dy}{dx} = \frac{f'(x)g(x) - f(x)g'(x)}{[g(x)]^2}$$

$$f(x) = 2 - 3x \Rightarrow f'(x) = -3$$
$$g(x) = x + 4 \Rightarrow g'(x) = 1$$

Hence $\dfrac{dy}{dx} = \dfrac{(-3)(x + 4) - (2 - 3x)(1)}{(x + 4)^2}$

> Using **4**

Simplifying, gives $\dfrac{dy}{dx} = \dfrac{-14}{(x + 4)^2}$

(b) $y = \dfrac{\sin 3x}{x^2 + 1} = \dfrac{u}{v}$

$$u = \sin 3x \Rightarrow \frac{du}{dx} = 3\cos 3x$$

$$v = x^2 + 1 \Rightarrow \frac{dv}{dx} = 2x$$

$$\frac{dy}{dx} = \frac{v\dfrac{du}{dx} - u\dfrac{dv}{dx}}{v^2}$$

> Using **3**

$$\frac{dy}{dx} = \frac{(x^2 + 1)(3\cos 3x) - (\sin 3x)(2x)}{(x^2 + 1)^2}$$

$$\frac{dy}{dx} = \frac{3(x^2 + 1)\cos 3x - 2x(\sin 3x)}{(x^2 + 1)^2}$$

> This cannot be simplified very much but it is usual to write numbers first, then polynomials, then other functions.

(c) $y = \dfrac{e^{4x}}{2 + \cos 5x}$

> This is once again a quotient.

$$\frac{dy}{dx} = \frac{(4e^{4x})(2 + \cos 5x) - (-5\sin 5x)(e^{4x})}{(2 + \cos 5x)^2}$$

> Using **3** or **4**

$$\frac{dy}{dx} = \frac{e^{4x}(8 + 4\cos 5x + 5\sin 5x)}{(2 + \cos 5x)^2}$$

> You may need to write $u = e^{4x}$ and $v = 2 + \cos 5x$ etc. With experience, you should be able to write down the second line of the answer directly.

Worked example 4

Differentiate each of the following with respect to x:
(a) $4\tan 3x$ **(b)** $\operatorname{cosec}(x^2 + 3)$ **(c)** $e^{-2x}\sec 4x$

6

(a) $y = 4\tan 3x \Rightarrow \dfrac{dy}{dx} = 12\sec^2 3x$

> Using **5**

(b) Let $u = x^2 + 3$, then $y = \operatorname{cosec} u$

$$\frac{dy}{du} = -\operatorname{cosec} u \cot u$$

> Using **5**

$$\frac{du}{dx} = 2x$$

$$y = \operatorname{cosec}(x^2+3) \Rightarrow \frac{dy}{dx} = -2x\operatorname{cosec}(x^2+3)\cot(x^2+3)$$

> By the chain rule.

(c) $y = e^{-2x}\sec 4x$

> The product rule must be used.

Let $y = u \times v$ where $u = e^{-2x}$ and $v = \sec 4x$

$$\frac{du}{dx} = -2e^{-2x} \quad \text{and} \quad \frac{dv}{dx} = 4\sec 4x \tan 4x$$

> Using **5**

$$\frac{dy}{dx} = u\frac{dv}{dx} + v\frac{du}{dx}$$

> Using **1**

$$\frac{dy}{dx} = e^{-2x}(4\sec 4x \tan 4x) + (\sec 4x)(-2e^{-2x})$$

$$= 2e^{-2x}\sec 4x(2\tan 4x - 1)$$

Worked example 5

A curve is defined for $x > 0$ by the equation $y = \dfrac{\ln x}{2x + 1}$.

(a) Find $\dfrac{dy}{dx}$.

(b) Hence find an equation for the normal to the curve at the point where $x = 1$.

(a) $\dfrac{dy}{dx} = \dfrac{(2x + 1)\left(\dfrac{1}{x}\right) - 2\ln x}{(2x + 1)^2}$.

(b) When $x = 1$, $y = \dfrac{\ln 1}{3} = 0$.

Gradient of curve at this point is $\dfrac{3 - 2\ln 1}{3^2} = \dfrac{1}{3}$.

Hence the gradient of the normal at this point is -3.

Equation of the normal is $y = -3(x - 1)$ or $3x + y = 3$.

REVISION EXERCISE 6

1 Differentiate with respect to x:

(a) $x^3 \ln x$ (b) $e^{5x} \cos x$ (c) $(x^2 - 3x)\sin 2x$

(d) $e^{2x} \ln x$ (e) $x^4 \cos 3x$ (f) $\sin 4x \cos 3x$

2 Find $\dfrac{dy}{dx}$ for each of the following curves.

(a) $\dfrac{e^{2x}}{x}$ (b) $\dfrac{\cos x}{x + 1}$ (c) $\dfrac{\ln x}{x^3}$ (d) $\dfrac{x^3}{\sin 2x}$

(e) $\dfrac{x}{\sqrt{x + 1}}$ (f) $\dfrac{x^2}{\ln x}$

3 (a) Given that $y = \dfrac{3 - 7x}{2x - 5}$ show that $\dfrac{dy}{dx} = \dfrac{29}{(2x - 5)^2}$

(b) Given that $y = \dfrac{2 + x^2}{1 + x^2}$ show that $\dfrac{dy}{dx} = \dfrac{-2x}{(1 + x^2)^2}$

4 Assuming only the derivatives of $\sin x$ and $\cos x$, use the quotient rule to prove that:

(a) the derivative of $\dfrac{\cos x}{\sin x}$ is $\dfrac{-1}{\sin^2 x}$

(b) the derivative of $\dfrac{\sin x + \cos x}{\cos x}$ is $\dfrac{1}{\cos^2 x}$

5 A curve has equation $y = \dfrac{4 + 3x}{1 + x^2}$.

   (a) Find $\dfrac{dy}{dx}$.

   (b) Find the coordinates of the stationary points of the curve and determine whether each stationary point is a maximum or minimum point.

6 A curve has equation $y = (x + 2)e^{-x}$. Find the coordinates of the stationary point of the curve and determine its nature.

7 A curve is defined for $x > -5$ by $y = x^2\sqrt{x + 5}$.

   (a) Find $\dfrac{dy}{dx}$.

   (b) Find the coordinates of the stationary points of the curve.

8 The diagram below shows the curve defined for $x > 0$ by the equation $y = 1 - 4x^2 \ln x$.

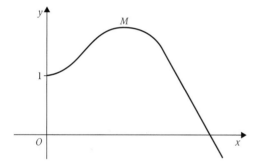

   (a) Find $\dfrac{dy}{dx}$.

   (b) Find an equation of the tangent to the curve at the point where $x = 1$.

   (c) Determine the coordinates of the maximum point M.

   (d) Find the value of $\dfrac{d^2y}{dx^2}$ at the point M.

9 A curve has equation $y = e^{-x}(\cos 2x + \sin 2x)$.

   (a) Show that the stationary points of the curve occur when $\tan 2x = \dfrac{1}{3}$.

   (b) Find an equation of the tangent to the curve at the point $(0, 1)$.

   (c) Show that $\dfrac{d^2y}{dx^2} + 2\dfrac{dy}{dx} + 5y = 0$ at all points on the curve.

10 A curve, defined for $x > 0$, has equation $y = \dfrac{x^2 - \ln x}{x^2}$.

    (a) Show that $\dfrac{dy}{dx} = \dfrac{2\ln x - 1}{x^3}$.

    (b) Find $\dfrac{d^2y}{dx^2}$.

    (c) Show that the curve has a single stationary point. Find its coordinates and determine whether it is a maximum or minimum point.

Test yourself	What to review
	If your answer is incorrect:
1 Differentiate the following with respect to x: **(a)** $e^{-x}\cos x$ **(b)** $x^5 e^{2x}$ **(c)** $e^{-3x}\sin 2x$ **(d)** $x^2 \ln 3x$.	Review Advancing Maths for AQA C3C4 pages 97–102.
2 Find $\dfrac{dy}{dx}$ for each of the following expressions: **(a)** $y = \dfrac{x^3}{x-1}$ **(b)** $y = \dfrac{x}{1+\sin x}$ **(c)** $y = \dfrac{\cos 3x}{x+1}$ **(d)** $y = \dfrac{x^3}{\ln x}$	Review Advancing Maths for AQA C3C4 pages 102–106.
3 Differentiate each of the following with respect to x: **(a)** $y = 3\tan 4x$ **(b)** $y = 5\sec(x^3+1)$ **(c)** $y = \operatorname{cosec}(2-5x)$ **(d)** $y = 4\cot(1-x)$	Review Advancing Maths for AQA C3C4 pages 108–111.
4 Find the coordinates of the stationary point of the curve with equation $y = (x-3)e^{2x}$.	Review Advancing Maths for AQA C3C4 page 100.
5 Find the gradient of the curve with equation $y = \dfrac{\ln x}{x^2}$ at the point where $x = 2$.	Review Advancing Maths for AQA C3C4 page 104.

Test yourself   ANSWERS

1 (a) $-e^{-x}(\sin x + \cos x)$ **(b)** $x^4 e^{2x}(5 + 2x)$ **(c)** $e^{-3x}(2\cos 2x - 3\sin 2x)$
(d) $x + 2x \ln 3x$

2 (a) $\dfrac{x^2(2x - 3)}{(x - 1)^2}$ **(b)** $\dfrac{(1 + \sin x) - x \cos x}{(1 + \sin x)^2}$
(c) $\dfrac{(x + 1)(-3\sin 3x) - \cos 3x}{(x + 1)^2}$ **(d)** $\dfrac{x^2(3\ln x - 1)}{(\ln x)^2}$

3 (a) $12\sec^2 4x$ **(b)** $15x^2 \sec(x^3 + 1)\tan(x^3 + 1)$
(c) $5\csc(2 - 5x)\cot(2 - 5x)$
(d) $4\csc^2(1 - x)$

4 $\left(\dfrac{2}{5}, -\dfrac{1}{2}e^5\right)$

5 $\dfrac{1 - 2\ln 2}{8}$

6

CHAPTER 7

Numerical solutions of equations and iterative methods

Key points to remember

1 If the graph of $y = f(x)$ is continuous over the interval $a \leqslant x \leqslant b$, and $f(a)$ and $f(b)$ have different signs, then at least one root of the equation $f(x) = 0$ must lie in the interval $a < x < b$.

2 Cobweb and/or staircase diagrams can be drawn to illustrate whether convergence takes place or not for iterations of the form $x_{n+1} = g(x_n)$.

3 An iteration of the form $x_{n+1} = g(x_n)$ converges when the gradient of $y = g(x)$ at the point of intersection with the line $y = x$ satisfies the condition $|g'(x)| < 1$, provided a suitable value for x_1 is chosen.

Worked example 1

Show that the equation $x^3 + \sin 2x = 5$ has a root between 1.7 and 1.8.

The equation can be written as $x^3 + \sin 2x - 5 = 0$.

Let $f(x) \quad = x^3 + \sin 2x - 5$
$\quad \quad f(1.7) \quad = 1.7^3 + \sin 3.4 - 5 = -0.3425...$
$\quad \quad f(1.8) \quad = 1.8^3 + \sin 3.6 - 5 = 0.389...$

Since the graph of $y = f(x)$ is continuous, the change of sign indicates that a root of $f(x) = 0$ lies between 1.7 and 1.8.

Using **1**

Worked example 2

(a) Sketch the graphs of $y = \ln x$ and $y = 4 - x$ on the same axes and hence explain why the equation $x - 4 + \ln x = 0$ has a single root α.

(b) Verify that $\alpha = 2.926$ correct to 3 decimal places.

(a)

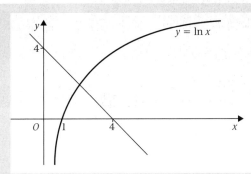

There is a single point of intersection.
It follows that the equation $\ln x = 4 - x$ has a single root.
This can be rearranged to give $x - 4 + \ln x = 0$.
Hence the equation $x - 4 + \ln x = 0$ has a single root, α.
The sketch indicates that α lies between 1 and 4.

(b) Let $f(x) = x - 4 + \ln x$
$$f(2.9255) = 2.9255 - 4 + \ln 2.9255 = -0.00103\ldots$$
$$f(2.9265) = 2.9265 - 4 + \ln 2.9265 = +0.00307\ldots$$
The change of sign indicates that the equation has a root between 2.9255 and 2.9265.

Using **I**

The equation has only one root, α.
Hence $\alpha = 2.926$ (correct to 3 decimal places).

7

Worked example 3

The curve with equation $y = x^3 + 5x - 7$ crosses the x-axis at the point where $x = \alpha$.

(a) Show that α lies between 1.1 and 1.2.

(b) Show that the equation $x^3 + 5x - 7 = 0$ can be rearranged into the form $x = \dfrac{7 - x^3}{5}$.

(c) Use the iterative formula $x_{n+1} = \dfrac{7 - x_n^3}{5}$, with $x_1 = 1.1$ to find x_3, giving your answer to four decimal places.

(d) Sketch the graphs of $y = \dfrac{7 - x^3}{5}$ and $y = x$ on the same axes and draw a cobweb or staircase diagram to show how convergence takes place, indicating the positions of x_1, x_2 and x_3 on the x-axis.

(a) Let $f(x) = x^3 + 5x - 7$

$f(1.1) = 1.1^3 + 5.5 - 7 = -0.169$

$f(1.2) = 1.2^3 + 6 - 7 = 0.728$

Since the graph of $y = f(x)$ is continuous, the change of sign indicates that α lies between 1.1 and 1.2.

> Using **1**

(b) $x^3 + 5x - 7 = 0$

$$5x = 7 - x^3$$

$$x = \frac{7 - x^3}{5}$$

(c) $x_2 = \dfrac{7 - 1.1^3}{5}$

$= 1.1338$

$x_3 = \dfrac{7 - (1.1338)^3}{5}$

$= 1.1085$

(d)

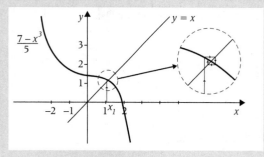

Worked example 4

(a) Sketch the graph of $y = \sin^{-1} x$ for $-1 \leqslant x \leqslant 1$.

(b) (i) By drawing a suitable straight line on your sketch, show that the equation $2x + \sin^{-1} x = 1$ has only one root.

(ii) Given that the root of this equation is α, show that $0 < \alpha < 0.5$.

(c) (i) Show that the equation $2x + \sin^{-1} x = 1$ can be rearranged into the form

$$x = \frac{1}{2}(1 - \sin^{-1} x)$$

(ii) Use the iteration $x_{n+1} = \dfrac{1}{2}(1 - \sin^{-1} x_n)$ with $x_1 = 0.3$ to find the value of x_3, giving your answer to four significant figures.

(a)

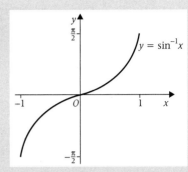

(b) (i) The line $y = 1 - 2x$ intersects the graph from part **(a)** in exactly one point. Hence the equation $\sin^{-1} x = 1 - 2x$ has only one root.

(ii) Let $f(x) = 2x + \sin^{-1} x - 1$.

$$f(0) = -1$$
$$f(0.5) = 0.52...$$

Since $y = f(x)$ is continuous, the change of sign indicates that the root α lies in the interval $0 < \alpha < 0.5$.

(c) (i) The equation $2x + \sin^{-1} x = 1$ can be rearranged to give $2x = 1 - \sin^{-1} x$.

Hence $x = \frac{1}{2}(1 - \sin^{-1} x)$.

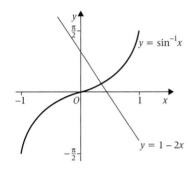

(ii) Using $x_{n+1} = \frac{1}{2}(1 - \sin^{-1} x_n)$ with $x_1 = 0.3$ gives

$$x_2 = \frac{1}{2}(1 - \sin^{-1} 0.3) = 0.34765...$$

and hence $x_3 = \frac{1}{2}(1 - \sin^{-1} 0.34765...) = 0.3224662...$

Therefore, $x_3 = 0.3225$ to four significant figures.

REVISION EXERCISE 7

1 Show that the equation $x^2 + \cos 3x = 2$ has a root between 1.49 and 1.50.

2 Verify that the root of the equation $x^5 + 5x^3 - 17 = 0$ is 1.355, correct to three decimal places.

3 (a) (i) Sketch the graphs of $y = e^x$ and the line $y = -x$ on the same axes to show that the equation $x + e^x = 0$ has a single root α.

(ii) Show that α lies between -1 and 0.

(b) Use the iterative formula $x_{n+1} = -e^{x_n}$, with $x_1 = -1$ to find the values of x_2 and x_3, giving your answers to three decimal places.

4 (a) Given that $f(x) = 3 + 4x - x^4$, show that $f(x) = 0$ has a root α between 1 and 2.

(b) The iterative formula with $x_{n+1} = (3 + 4x_n)^{\frac{1}{4}}$ with $x_1 = 2$ may be used to find α. Find the values of x_2 and x_3, giving your answers to 2 decimal places.

5 (a) Show that the equation $x^3 + 2x - 4 = 0$ has a root α between 1.1 and 1.2.

(b) (i) Show that the equation $x^3 + 2x - 4 = 0$ can be rewritten in the form

$$x = (4 - 2x)^{\frac{1}{3}}.$$

(ii) Use the iterative formula $x_{n+1} = (4 - 2x_n)^{\frac{1}{3}}$, with $x_1 = 1$ to find the values of x_2 and x_3, giving your answers to 2 decimal places.

(c) Copy the graphs of $y = (4 - 2x)^{\frac{1}{3}}$ and $y = x$ and the position of x_1, and draw a cobweb or staircase diagram to show how convergence takes place, indicating the positions of x_2 and x_3 on the x-axis.

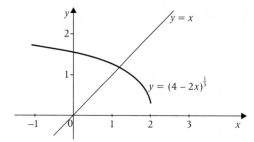

6 (a) (i) Sketch the graph of $y = x^3$ and a suitable straight line on the same axes to show that the equation $x^3 + 3x - 12 = 0$ has a single root β.

(ii) Verify that β lies between 1 and 2.

(b) (i) Show that the equation $x^3 + 3x - 12 = 0$ can be rearranged into

$$x = (12 - 3x)^{\frac{1}{3}}.$$

(ii) Use an iterative formula of the form $x_{n+1} = [f(x_n)]^{\frac{1}{3}}$ with $x_1 = 2$ to find the values of x_2, x_3 and x_4, giving your answers to three decimal places.

7 The sequence given by the iterative formula

$x_{n+1} = 2(1 + e^{-x_n})$, with $x_1 = 2$, converges to γ.

  (a) Find the value of γ correct to 3 decimal places, proving that your answer does indeed have this degree of accuracy.

  (b) Write down an equation for which γ is a root.

8 The curve with equation $y = 4 + 3x - x^3$ crosses the x-axis at the point where $x = \alpha$.

  (a) Show that α lies between 1 and 3.

  (b) Show that the equation $4 + 3x - x^3 = 0$ can be rearranged into the form $x = \sqrt[3]{4 + 3x}$

  (c) Use the iterative formula $x_{n+1} = \sqrt[3]{4 + 3x_n}$, with $x_1 = 1.5$ to find x_2 and x_3, giving your answers to 2 decimal places.

  (d) Copy the graphs of $y = \sqrt[3]{4 + 3x}$ and $y = x$ and the position of x_1, and draw a cobweb or staircase diagram to show how convergence takes place, indicating the positions of x_2 and x_3 on the x-axis.

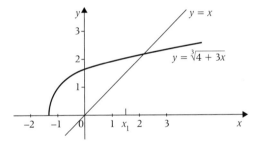

9 (a) Sketch the graph of $y = \tan^{-1} x$.

  (b) **(i)** By drawing a suitable straight line on your sketch, show that the equation $\tan^{-1} x = 3 - 5x$ has only one root.

     (ii) Given that the root of this equation is α, show that $0 < \alpha < 1$.

  (c) **(i)** Show that the equation $\tan^{-1} x = 3 - 5x$ can be rearranged into the form $x = \frac{1}{5}(3 - \tan^{-1} x)$

     (ii) Use the iteration $x_{n+1} = \frac{1}{5}(3 - \tan^{-1} x_n)$ with $x_1 = 0.5$ to find the value of x_3, giving your answer to four significant figures.

Test yourself	What to review
	If your answer is incorrect:

1 The equation $x^3 + 5x^2 - 20 = 0$ has a single root α. Prove that the value of α is equal to 1.725 correct to three decimal places.

Review Advancing Maths for AQA C3C4 pages 116–122.

2 Find pairs of consecutive integers between which the roots of the equation $x^3 - 4x^2 - 11x + 29 = 0$ lie.

Review Advancing Maths for AQA C3C4 pages 116–122.

3 Use the iterative formula $x_{n+1} = \frac{2}{5}(2 + 3\tan^{-1}x_n)$,

with $x = 2$, to find the values of x_2 and x_3, giving your answers to three significant figures.

Review Advancing Maths for AQA C3C4 pages 122–126.

4 For each of the following sequences, find the values of x_2, x_3 and x_4 and state whether the sequence is convergent or not.

Review Advancing Maths for AQA C3C4 pages 122–126.

   (a) $x_{n+1} = \dfrac{7 - 4x_n}{6}$, $x_1 = 1$

   (b) $x_{n+1} = \dfrac{2}{1 - 3x_n}$, $x_1 = -1$

5 **(a)** Sketch on the same axes the graphs of $y = 2e^x$ and $y = 1 - 3x$.

Review Advancing Maths for AQA C3C4 pages 120–121.

   (b) Use your graph from **(a)** to explain why the equation $2e^x - 1 + 3x = 0$ has a single root, α.

   (c) Prove that α lies between –0.4 and –0.2.

6 **(a)** Find a cubic polynomial equation which is a rearrangement of the equation $x = \sqrt[3]{2 + x}$.

Review Advancing Maths for AQA C3C4 pages 126–130.

   (b) The iterative formula $x_{n+1} = \sqrt[3]{2 + x_n}$ is to be used with $x_1 = 0$. Find the values of x_2, x_3 and x_4 to four decimal places, and draw a cobweb or staircase diagram to show whether the sequence converges or diverges.

2 {−3, −2}, {1, 2}, {5, 6}

3 2.13, 2.16

4 **(a)** $\dfrac{1}{2}$, $\dfrac{5}{6}$, $\dfrac{11}{18}$ convergent to limit 0.7 **(b)** $\dfrac{1}{2}$, −4, $\dfrac{2}{13}$ not convergent

5 **(a)**

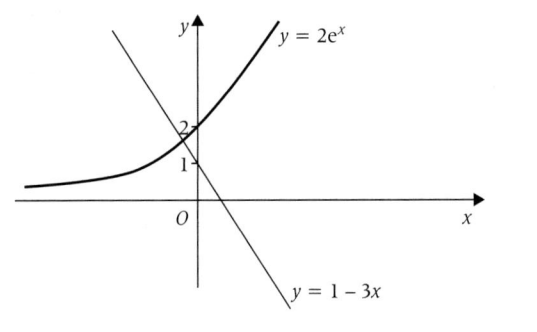

(b) Curve and line have a single point of intersection. At intersection point $2e^x = 1 - 3x$.

Hence $2e^x - 1 + 3x = 0$ has a single root.

6 **(a)** $x^3 = 2 + x$, hence $x^3 - x - 2 = 0$

(b) 1.2599; 1.4828; 1.5158

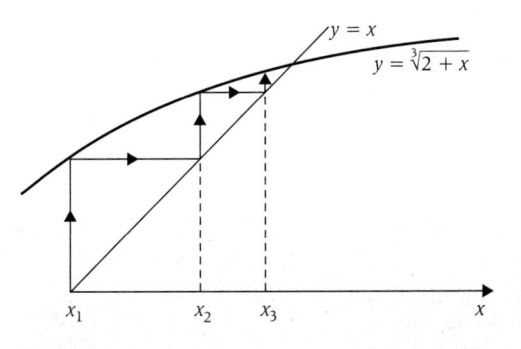

Sequence converges.

CHAPTER 8

Integration by inspection and substitution

Key points to remember

(where c is the constant of integration)

1 For constants a, b and n, where $n \neq -1$,

$$\int (ax + b)^n \, dx = \frac{1}{a(n + 1)} (ax + b)^{n+1} + c$$

2 For constants a and b,

$$\int e^{ax+b} \, dx = \frac{1}{a} e^{ax+b} + c$$

3 For x in radians,

$$\int \cos x \, dx = \sin x + c$$

$$\int \sin x \, dx = -\cos x + c$$

$$\int \sec^2 x \, dx = \tan x + c$$

4 For constants a and b and x in radians,

$$\int \cos(ax + b) \, dx = \frac{1}{a}\sin(ax + b) + c$$

$$\int \sin(ax + b) \, dx = -\frac{1}{a}\cos(ax + b) + c$$

$$\int \sec^2(ax + b) \, dx = \frac{1}{a}\tan(ax + b) + c$$

5 For a constant a and x in radians,

$$\int \operatorname{cosec} ax \cot ax \, dx = -\frac{1}{a}\operatorname{cosec} ax + c$$

$$\int \sec ax \tan ax \, dx = \frac{1}{a}\sec ax + c$$

$$\int \operatorname{cosec}^2 ax \, dx = -\frac{1}{a}\cot ax + c$$

Key points to remember *continued*

6 $\int \frac{f'(x)}{f(x)} \, dx = \ln|f(x)| + c$

7 For a constant a, and x in radians,

$\int \tan ax \, dx = \frac{1}{a}\ln|\sec ax| + c$

$\int \cot ax \, dx = \frac{1}{a}\ln|\sin ax| + c$

$\int \sec ax \, dx = \frac{1}{a}\ln|\sec ax + \tan ax| + c$

$\int \operatorname{cosec} ax \, dx = -\frac{1}{a}\ln|\operatorname{cosec} ax + \cot ax| + c$

8 These results are used in integration by substitution

$$\dots dx = \dots \frac{dx}{du} \, du \quad \text{and} \quad \dots du = \dots \frac{du}{dx} \, dx$$

Worked example 1

Find $\int \frac{1}{2(2x + 5)^3} \, dx$.

$-\frac{(2x+5)^{-2}}{2} \qquad \frac{du}{du} = \frac{1}{2}$

$\int \frac{1}{2(2x + 5)^3} \, dx = \frac{1}{2}\int \frac{1}{(2x + 5)^3} \, dx$ — Taking out the constant.

$= \frac{1}{2}\int (2x + 5)^{-3} \, dx$ — Using $\frac{1}{y^3} = y^{-3}$.

$= \frac{1}{2} \times \frac{1}{2(-3 + 1)}(2x + 5)^{-3+1} + c$ — Using **1** with $a = 2$, $b = 5$, $n = -3$.

$= -\frac{1}{8}(2x + 5)^{-2} + c$ — Remembering to add the constant of integration.

$-\frac{1}{8}(2x+5)^{2}$

Worked example 2

(a) Find **(i)** $\int e^{3x-1}$ **(ii)** $\int \frac{1}{\sqrt{6x + 2}} \, dx$.

(b) Hence find the exact value of $\int_{-\frac{1}{3}}^{\frac{1}{3}} (e^{3x-1} - \frac{1}{\sqrt{6x + 2}}) \, dx$.

8

(a) (i) $\int e^{3x-1}\,dx = \dfrac{1}{3}\,e^{3x-1} + c$

> Using **2** with $a = 3$ and $b = -1$.

(ii) $\int \dfrac{1}{\sqrt{6x+2}}\,dx = \int (6x+2)^{-\frac{1}{2}}\,dx$

> Writing in the form $(ax+b)^n$.

$$= \dfrac{1}{6\left(-\dfrac{1}{2}+1\right)}\,(6x+2)^{\frac{1}{2}} + c$$

> Using **1** with $a = 6$, $b = 2$, $n = -\dfrac{1}{2}$.

$$= \dfrac{1}{3}\,\sqrt{6x+2} + c$$

(b) $\displaystyle\int_{-\frac{1}{3}}^{\frac{1}{3}} \left(e^{3x-1} - \dfrac{1}{\sqrt{6x+2}}\right)\,dx = \dfrac{1}{3}\left[e^{3x-1} - \sqrt{6x+2}\right]_{-\frac{1}{3}}^{\frac{1}{3}}$

> Using answers from part **(a)**.

$$= \dfrac{1}{3}\left\{\left(e^0 - \sqrt{4}\right) - \left(e^{-2} - 0\right)\right\}$$

> Using $F(\frac{1}{3}) - F(-\frac{1}{3})$, where $F(x) = \dfrac{1}{3}\left[e^{3x-1} - \sqrt{6x+2}\right]$.

$$= -\dfrac{1}{3}\,(1 + e^{-2})$$

> $e^0 = 1$

Worked example 3

(a) Differentiate $(1 + \cos 2x)$ with respect to x.

(b) Hence, find the **exact** value of $\displaystyle\int_0^{\frac{\pi}{4}} \dfrac{\sin 2x}{(1 + \cos 2x)}\,dx$.

(a) $\dfrac{d}{dx}(1 + \cos 2x) = -2\sin 2x$

> Using $\dfrac{d}{dx}(\cos kx) = -k\sin kx$.

(b) $\displaystyle\int_0^{\frac{\pi}{4}} \dfrac{\sin 2x}{(1 + \cos 2x)}\,dx = -\dfrac{1}{2}\int_0^{\frac{\pi}{4}} \dfrac{-2\sin 2x}{(1 + \cos 2x)}\,dx$

> Writing in the form $\int \dfrac{f'(x)}{f(x)}\,dx$.

$$= -\dfrac{1}{2}\left[\ln(1 + \cos 2x)\right]_0^{\frac{\pi}{4}}$$

> Using **6** with $f(x) = 1 + \cos 2x$.

$$= -\dfrac{1}{2}\left\{\ln\left(1 + \cos\dfrac{\pi}{2}\right) - \ln(1 + \cos 0)\right\}$$

$$= -\dfrac{1}{2}\{\ln 1 - \ln 2\}$$

> $\cos\dfrac{\pi}{2} = 0$, $\cos 0 = 1$ and $\ln 1 = 0$.

$$= \dfrac{1}{2}\ln 2$$

> $\dfrac{1}{2}\ln 2$ is an exact value. Do not give a decimal approximation.

Worked example 4

Find $\int \dfrac{\sin^2 3x - \cos^2 3x}{\sin^2 3x \cos^2 3x}\, dx$.

$$\int \frac{\sin^2 3x - \cos^2 3x}{\sin^2 3x \cos^2 3x}\, dx$$

$$= \int\left(\frac{\sin^2 3x}{\sin^2 3x \cos^2 3x} - \frac{\cos^2 3x}{\sin^2 3x \cos^2 3x}\right) dx$$ — Split the fraction.

$$= \int\left(\frac{1}{\cos^2 3x} - \frac{1}{\sin^2 3x}\right) dx$$ — Cancelling

$$= \int(\sec^2 3x - \operatorname{cosec}^2 3x)\, dx$$ — Use $\dfrac{1}{\cos\theta} = \sec\theta$ and $\dfrac{1}{\sin\theta} = \operatorname{cosec}\theta$.

$$= \frac{1}{3}\tan 3x - \left(-\frac{1}{3}\cot 3x\right) + c$$ — Use **4** with $a = 3$ and $b = 0$; Use **5** with $a = 3$.

$$= \frac{1}{3}(\tan 3x + \cot 3x) + c$$

Worked example 5

Use the substitution $u = x^2 + 7$ to find $\int 2x^3(x^2 + 7)^6\, dx$.

Let $u = x^2 + 7 \Rightarrow \dfrac{du}{dx} = 2x \Rightarrow du = 2x\, dx$

$$\int 2x^3(x^2 + 7)^6\, dx = \int x^2(x^2 + 7)^6\, 2x\, dx$$

$$= \int(u - 7)u^6\, du = \int(u^7 - 7u^6)\, du$$ — Using **8**

$$= \frac{u^8}{8} - u^7 + c$$

$$= \frac{1}{8}(x^2 + 7)^7(x^2 + 7 - 8) + c$$ — The final answer must be in terms of the original variable, x.

$$\int 2x^3(x^2 + 7)^6\, dx = \frac{1}{8}(x^2 + 7)^7(x^2 - 1) + c$$

Worked example 6

Use the substitution $u = 1 + \sin x$ to evaluate $\displaystyle\int_0^{\frac{\pi}{2}} \frac{\cos^3 x}{1 + \sin x}\, dx$.

Let $u = 1 + \sin x \Rightarrow \dfrac{du}{dx} = \cos x \Rightarrow du = \cos x\, dx$

When $x = \dfrac{\pi}{2}$, $u = 2$ and when $x = 0$, $u = 1$. •———————— | Finding the limits for u. |

$$\int_0^{\frac{\pi}{2}} \frac{\cos^3 x}{1 + \sin x}\, dx = \int_0^{\frac{\pi}{2}} \frac{\cos^2 x \cos x}{1 + \sin x}\, dx$$

$$= \int_0^{\frac{\pi}{2}} \frac{(1 - \sin^2 x)}{1 + \sin x} \cos x\, dx$$ •———— | Using the identity $\cos^2 x + \sin^2 x = 1$. |

$$= \int_1^2 \frac{1 - (u - 1)^2}{u}\, du$$ •———— | The position of the limits for u must match the the position of the corresponding limits for x. |

$$= \int_1^2 \frac{2u - u^2}{u}\, du$$ •———— | Simplifying the numerator. |

$$= \int_1^2 \left(\frac{2u}{u} - \frac{u^2}{u}\right) du = \int_1^2 (2 - u)\, du$$ •———— | Splitting the fraction. |

$$= \left[\left(2u - \frac{u^2}{2}\right)\right]_1^2$$

$$= (4 - 2) - \left(2 - \frac{1}{2}\right)$$

$$\int_0^{\frac{\pi}{2}} \frac{\cos^3 x}{1 + \sin x}\, dx = \frac{1}{2}$$

REVISION EXERCISE 8

1 (a) Find $\displaystyle\int 6(2x - 1)^8\, dx$.

(b) Hence evaluate $\displaystyle\int_0^1 6(2x - 1)^8\, dx$.

2 (a) Find **(i)** $\displaystyle\int e^{2x}\, dx$ **(ii)** $\displaystyle\int e^{-2x}\, dx$.

(b) Evaluate $\displaystyle\int_0^{\frac{1}{2}} \left(e^x - \frac{1}{e^x}\right)^2 dx$.

3 Find the area of the region bounded by the curve $y = \cos \frac{1}{2}x$, the coordinate axes and the line $x = 1$. Give your answer to three significant figures.

4 Find **(a)** $\displaystyle\int \sec^2 x\, dx$ **(b)** $\displaystyle\int \tan^2 x\, dx$ **(c)** $\displaystyle\int (1 - \tan x)^2\, dx$.

5 Find **(a)** $\int 4\operatorname{cosec}^2 2x\ dx$ **(b)** $\int 4\cot^2 2x\ dx$.

6 Evaluate $\displaystyle\int_0^{\frac{\pi}{9}} \sin\left(3x + \frac{2\pi}{3}\right) dx$.

7 (a) Differentiate $(x^3 + 9x)$ with respect to x.

   (b) Hence find $\displaystyle\int \frac{x^2 + 3}{x^3 + 9x}\ dx$.

   (c) Show that $\displaystyle\int_1^2 \frac{x^2 + 3}{x^3 + 9x}\ dx = \frac{1}{3}\ln\frac{13}{5}$.

8 (a) Find **(i)** $\displaystyle\int \frac{\sin x}{\cos x}\ dx$ **(ii)** $\displaystyle\int \frac{\sin x}{1 + \cos x}\ dx$.

   (b) Show that $\displaystyle\int_0^{\frac{\pi}{2}} \frac{\sin x}{1 + \cos x}\ dx = \ln 2$.

9 (a) Differentiate $(3 + \ln x)$ with respect to x.

   (b) Show that $= \displaystyle\int_1^e \frac{1}{x(3 + \ln x)}\ dx = \ln\frac{4}{3}$.

10 (a) Find $\displaystyle\int \frac{4e^{2x}}{e^{2x} + 2}\ dx$.

   (b) Hence find the value of $\displaystyle\int_0^{\ln 2} \frac{4e^{2x}}{e^{2x} + 2}\ dx$, giving your answer in the form $\ln k$.

11 Use the substitution $u = (x - 1)$ to find $\int x(x - 1)^8\ dx$.

12 Use the substitution $u = \cos x$ to find $\int \cos^5 x \sin x\ dx$.

13 Use the substitution $u = (x^2 + 3)$ to find

   (a) $\displaystyle\int 10x(x^2 + 3)^{\frac{3}{2}}\ dx$ **(b)** $\int x \sin(x^2 + 3)\ dx$
   (c) $\int x^3 \sqrt{x^2 + 3}\ dx$.

14 Use the substitution $u = (x^3 + 3x)$ to find

   $\int (x^2 + 1)e^{(x^3 + 3x)}\ dx$.

15 Use the substitution $u = (e^x + 2)$ to find $\displaystyle\int \frac{e^{2x}}{e^x + 2}\ dx$.

16 Use the substitution $u = x^2 + 1$ to evaluate $\displaystyle\int_0^{\sqrt{3}} x\sqrt{x^2 + 1}\ dx$.

8

17 Use the substitution $u = x^2 - 1$ to evaluate $\int_1^2 2x \sec^2 (x^2 - 1) \, dx$.

Give your answer to three significant figures.

18 Use the substitution $u = e^{2x} + 1$ to evaluate $\int_0^{\frac{1}{2}} \frac{2e^{4x}}{e^{2x} + 1} \, dx$.

19 Use the substitution $u = \sec 2x$ to evaluate $\int_0^{\frac{\pi}{6}} \sec^3 2x \tan 2x \, dx$.

20 Use the substitution $u = \sin x$ to find the area of the region bounded

by the curve $y = \cos^3 x$, the coordinate axes and the line $x = \frac{\pi}{6}$.

Test yourself	What to review
	If your answer is incorrect:
1 **(a)** Find $\int (2 - 3x)^5 \, dx$. **(b)** Find $\int_0^{\frac{\pi}{4}} \cos\left(2x + \frac{\pi}{2}\right) dx$.	Review Advancing Maths for AQA C3C4 pages 136–142.
2 Find $\int_0^2 \frac{6x^2}{x^3 + 1} \, dx$, giving your answer in a simplified exact form.	Review Advancing Maths for AQA C3C4 pages 143–146.
3 Use the substitution $u = 2 + \ln x$ to show that $\int_1^e \frac{2(2 + \ln x)}{x} \, dx = 5$.	Review Advancing Maths for AQA C3C4 pages 146–151.
4 Use the substitution $u = e^{2x} + 1$ to find $\int \frac{10e^{2x}}{(e^{2x} + 1)^6} \, dx$.	Review Advancing Maths for AQA C3C4 pages 146–151.
5 Use the substitution $u = \tan x$ to evaluate $\int_0^{\frac{\pi}{4}} \sec^4 x \, dx$.	Review Advancing Maths for AQA C3C4 pages 146–151.

Test yourself ANSWERS

5 $\frac{4}{3}$

4 $-\frac{1}{(e^{2x} + 1)^5} + c$

2 $\ln 81.$

1 **(a)** $-\frac{1}{18} (2 - 3x)^6 + c$ **(b)** $-\frac{1}{2}$.

CHAPTER 9

Integration by parts and use of further substitutions

Key points to remember

(where c is the constant of integration)

1 $\int u\dfrac{\mathrm{d}v}{\mathrm{d}x}\,\mathrm{d}x = uv - \int v\dfrac{\mathrm{d}u}{\mathrm{d}x}\,\mathrm{d}x$ is known as the integration by parts formula and is given, in this form, in the examination formulae booklet.

2 In the examination, the method of integration by parts is most commonly, although not exclusively, used to solve integrals of the form

$\int x^n \sin mx\,\mathrm{d}x;$

$\int x^n \cos mx\,\mathrm{d}x;$

$\int x^n \mathrm{e}^{mx}\,\mathrm{d}x;$

$\int x^n \ln mx\,\mathrm{d}x.$

> For C3 examination papers taken in 2007 and subsequent years, the use of the two standard integrals
>
> $$\int \frac{1}{a^2 + x^2}\,\mathrm{d}x = \frac{1}{a}\tan^{-1}\left(\frac{x}{a}\right) + c \quad \text{and} \quad \int \frac{1}{\sqrt{a^2 - x^2}}\,\mathrm{d}x = \sin^{-1}\left(\frac{x}{a}\right) + c$$
>
> has been removed from the C3 specification.

9

Worked example 1

Find $\int \dfrac{x}{\mathrm{e}^{\frac{1}{2}x}}\,\mathrm{d}x$.

$$\int \frac{x}{\mathrm{e}^{\frac{1}{2}x}}\,\mathrm{d}x = \int x\,\mathrm{e}^{-\frac{1}{2}x}\,\mathrm{d}x$$

Using $\dfrac{1}{\mathrm{e}^{kx}} = \mathrm{e}^{-kx}$ to write integral in the form $\int x^n \mathrm{e}^{mx}\,\mathrm{d}x$.

$$\int x\,\mathrm{e}^{-\frac{1}{2}x}\,\mathrm{d}x$$

To reduce the power of x, use $u = x$ and $\dfrac{\mathrm{d}v}{\mathrm{d}x} = \mathrm{e}^{-\frac{1}{2}x}$.

$$\int u\,\frac{\mathrm{d}v}{\mathrm{d}x}\,\mathrm{d}x = uv - \int v\,\frac{\mathrm{d}u}{\mathrm{d}x}\,\mathrm{d}x$$

Using **1**

$$u = x \Rightarrow \frac{du}{dx} = 1$$

$$\frac{dv}{dx} = e^{-\frac{1}{2}x} \Rightarrow v = -2e^{-\frac{1}{2}x}$$

Using $\int e^{kx}\,dx = \frac{1}{k}e^{kx} + c.$

$$\int \frac{x}{e^{\frac{1}{2}x}}\,dx = \left[x(-2e^{-\frac{1}{2}x})\right] - \int\left(-2e^{-\frac{1}{2}x}\right)(1)dx$$

Using **I**

$$\int \frac{x}{e^{\frac{1}{2}x}}\,dx = -2xe^{-\frac{1}{2}x} + 2\int e^{-\frac{1}{2}x}\,dx$$

So $\int \frac{x}{e^{\frac{1}{2}x}}\,dx = -2xe^{-\frac{1}{2}x} - 4e^{-\frac{1}{2}x} + c$

Using $\int e^{kx}\,dx = \frac{1}{k}e^{kx} + c.$

Remember to add the *c*.

Worked example 2

Find the area of the region bounded by the curve

$y = x\cos 3x$ and the *x*-axis from $x = 0$ to $x = \frac{\pi}{6}$.

Area $= \int_0^{\frac{\pi}{6}} x\cos 3x\,dx$

Using area $\int_a^b y\,dx.$

$$\int u\frac{dv}{dx}\,dx = uv - \int v\frac{du}{dx}\,dx$$

Using **I**

$$u = x \Rightarrow \frac{du}{dx} = 1$$

and $\frac{dv}{dx} = \cos 3x \Rightarrow v = \frac{1}{3}\sin 3x$

Using $\int \cos kx\,dx = \frac{1}{k}\sin kx + c.$

$$\int_0^{\frac{\pi}{6}} x\cos 3x\,dx = \left[x\left(\frac{1}{3}\sin 3x\right)\right]_0^{\frac{\pi}{6}} - \int_0^{\frac{\pi}{6}}\left(\frac{1}{3}\sin 3x\right)(1)dx$$

Using **I**

$$= \frac{\pi}{18}\sin\frac{\pi}{2} - 0 - \left[-\frac{1}{9}\cos 3x\right]_0^{\frac{\pi}{6}}$$

Using $\int \sin kx\,dx = -\frac{1}{k}\cos kx + c.$

$$= \frac{\pi}{18} + \frac{1}{9}\left(\cos\frac{\pi}{2} - \cos 0\right) = \frac{\pi}{18} + \frac{1}{9}(0-1)$$

$$= \frac{\pi}{18} - \frac{1}{9}$$

Required area $= \frac{\pi - 2}{18}$

Worked example 3

Find $\displaystyle\int_1^3 (x^2 + 1)\ln x^3 \, dx$.

$(x^2 + 1)\ln x^3 = 3(x^2 + 1)\ln x$ ⟵ Using $\ln x^n = n\ln x$.

$\displaystyle\int_1^3 (x^2 + 1)\ln x^3 \, dx = \int_1^3 (3x^2 + 3)\ln x \, dx$

$\displaystyle\int u\frac{dv}{dx}\, dx = uv - \int v\frac{du}{dx}\, dx$ ⟵ Using ∎

with $u = \ln x \Rightarrow \dfrac{du}{dx} = \dfrac{1}{x}$

and $\dfrac{dv}{dx} = 3x^2 + 3 \Rightarrow v = (x^3 + 3x)$

$\displaystyle\int_1^3 (x^2 + 1)\ln x^3 \, dx = \Big[(\ln x)(x^3 + 3x)\Big]_1^3 - \int_1^3 (x^3 + 3x)\Big(\frac{1}{x}\Big) dx$ ⟵ Using ∎

$= \Big[(\ln 3)(36) - (\ln 1)(4)\Big] - \displaystyle\int_1^3 (x^2 + 3)\, dx$ ⟵ Simplifying $(x^3 + 3x)\dfrac{1}{x}$.

$= 36\ln 3 - \Big[\dfrac{x^3}{3} + 3x\Big]_1^3$

$= 36\ln 3 - \Big\{(9 + 9) - \Big(\dfrac{1}{3} + 3\Big)\Big\}$

$\displaystyle\int_1^3 (x^2 + 1)\ln x^3 \, dx = 36\ln 3 - 14\dfrac{2}{3}$

9

Worked example 4

Use integration by parts to find $\displaystyle\int (2x + 1)\sec^2 2x \, dx$.

$\displaystyle\int u\frac{dv}{dx}\, dx = uv - \int v\frac{du}{dx}\, dx$ ⟵ Using ∎

$\displaystyle\int (2x + 1)\sec^2 2x \, dx$

$u = (2x + 1) \Rightarrow \dfrac{du}{dx} = 2$

and $\dfrac{dv}{dx} = \sec^2 2x \Rightarrow v = \dfrac{1}{2}\tan 2x$ ⟵ Using $\displaystyle\int \sec^2 kx \, dx = \dfrac{1}{k}\tan kx + c$ which is in the exam formulae booklet.

$$\int (2x + 1)\sec^2 2x \, dx = (2x + 1)\left(\frac{1}{2}\tan 2x\right) - \int\left(\frac{1}{2}\tan 2x\right)(2) \, dx$$

Using **I**

$$= \frac{1}{2}(2x + 1)\tan 2x - \int \tan 2x \, dx$$

$$= \frac{1}{2}(2x + 1)\tan 2x - \int \frac{\sin 2x}{\cos 2x} \, dx$$

Using $\tan \theta = \frac{\sin \theta}{\cos \theta}$.

$$= \frac{1}{2}(2x + 1)\tan 2x + \frac{1}{2}\int \frac{-2\sin 2x}{\cos 2x} \, dx$$

$$= \frac{1}{2}(2x + 1)\tan 2x + \frac{1}{2}\ln|\cos 2x| + c$$

Using $\int \frac{f'(x)}{f(x)} \, dx = \ln|f(x)| + c$ with $f(x) = \cos 2x$.

Worked example 5

Use the substitution $x = 2 \sin \theta$ to show that

$$\int \frac{1}{\sqrt{4 - x^2}} \, dx = \sin^{-1}\left(\frac{x}{2}\right) + c, \text{ where } c \text{ is a constant.}$$

$$x = 2 \sin \theta \Rightarrow \frac{dx}{d\theta} = 2 \cos \theta \Rightarrow dx = 2 \cos \theta \, d\theta$$

Using $\frac{d}{d\theta}(\sin \theta) = \cos \theta$.

$$\int \frac{1}{\sqrt{4 - x^2}} \, dx = \int \frac{1}{\sqrt{4(1 - \sin^2 \theta)}} \, (2 \cos \theta \, d\theta)$$

$$= \int \frac{1}{\sqrt{4 \cos^2 \theta)}} \, (2 \cos \theta \, d\theta)$$

Using $\cos^2 \theta + \sin^2 \theta = 1$.

$$= \int 1 \, d\theta$$

$$= \theta + c$$

$$\int \frac{1}{\sqrt{4 - x^2}} \, dx = \sin^{-1}\left(\frac{x}{2}\right) + c$$

$x = 2 \sin \theta \Rightarrow \sin \theta = \frac{x}{2} \Rightarrow$

$\theta = \sin^{-1}\left(\frac{x}{2}\right).$

REVISION EXERCISE 9

1 Use integration by parts to find $\int x \cos x \, dx$.

2 Use integration by parts to find $\int xe^x \, dx$.

3 Find $\int x\ln x \, dx$.

4 Use integration by parts to evaluate $\int_0^{\frac{1}{2}} xe^{2x} \, dx$.

5 Show that the area of the region bounded by the curve $y = x \sin x$ and the x-axis from $x = 0$ to $x = \pi$ is equal to π.

6 Evaluate $\int_0^1 x \cos x \, dx$, giving your answer to four decimal places.

7 The curve C is defined by $y = x^2 \sin x$, $0 \le x \le \dfrac{\pi}{2}$.

   Find the area of the region bounded by the curve C, the

   x-axis and the line $x = \dfrac{\pi}{2}$.

8 Find $\int_1^2 (1 + x)e^{\frac{1}{2}x} \, dx$.

9 Show that $\int_2^e \ln x \, dx = 2 - \ln 4$.

10 Find $\int_0^1 (x + e^x)^2 \, dx$.

11 **(a)** Show that the substitution $t = (x^2 + 1)$ transforms

   $$\int_0^1 2x(x^2 + 1)^3 \ln (x^2 + 1) \, dx \quad \text{into} \quad \int_1^2 t^3 \ln t \, dt.$$

   (b) Hence, using integration by parts, find

   $$\int_0^1 2x(x^2 + 1)^3 \ln(x^2 + 1) \, dx$$

   giving your answer in an exact form.

12 **(a)** Use the substitution $x = \tan \theta$ to find $\int \dfrac{1}{1 + x^2} \, dx$.

   (b) Using the substitution $u = 1 + x^2$, or otherwise,

   find $\int \dfrac{x}{1 + x^2} \, dx$.

9

(c) Use integration by parts to show that

$$\int \frac{x}{1 + x^2} dx = x \tan^{-1} x - \int \tan^{-1} x \, dx.$$

(d) Hence, or otherwise, show that

$$\int_{0}^{1} \tan^{-1} x \, dx = \frac{\pi}{4} - \frac{1}{2} \ln 2.$$

Test yourself	What to review
	If your answer is incorrect:
1 Find $\int \frac{x}{e^{3x}} \, dx$.	Review Advancing Maths for AQA C3C4 pages 154–158.
2 Evaluate $\int_{0}^{1} x \sin 3x \, dx$ giving your answer to three decimal places.	Review Advancing Maths for AQA C3C4 pages 154–158.
3 Use integration by parts to find $\int_{1}^{2} (x + 1)\ln x \, dx$.	Review Advancing Maths for AQA C3C4 pages 154–158.
4 Using the substitution $2x = \sin \theta$, or otherwise, find $\int \frac{1}{\sqrt{1 - 4x^2}} \, dx$.	Review Advancing Maths for AQA C3C4 pages 158–161.
5 Use integration by parts to find $\int_{1}^{e} (x + \frac{1}{x^2})\ln x^2 \, dx$, leaving your answer in terms of e.	Review Advancing Maths for AQA C3C4 pages 154–158.

Test yourself ANSWERS

5 $\frac{5}{2} + \frac{4}{e} - \frac{e^2}{2}$

4 $\frac{1}{2}\sin^{-1} 2x + c$

3 $4\ln 2 - \frac{7}{4}$

2 0.346

1 $-\frac{1}{3}xe^{-3x} - \frac{1}{9}e^{-3x} + c$

CHAPTER 10

Volume of revolution and numerical integration

Key points to remember

1 When the region bounded by the curve $y = f(x)$, the x-axis and the lines $x = a$ and $x = b$ is rotated through 2π radians about the x-axis, the volume, V, of the solid generated is called the volume of revolution and is given by

$$V = \int_a^b \pi y^2 \, dx = \int_a^b \pi[f(x)]^2 \, dx$$

2 When the region bounded by the curve $x = g(y)$, the y-axis and the lines $y = c$ and $y = d$ is rotated through 2π radians about the y-axis, the volume, V, of the solid generated is given by

$$V = \int_c^d \pi x^2 \, dy = \int_c^d \pi[g(y)]^2 \, dy$$

3 In all the numerical methods of integration an improvement to the estimate can be obtained by increasing the number of steps (strips).

4 The mid-ordinate rule for n strips is

$$\int_a^b y \, dx \approx h \left(y_{\frac{1}{2}} + y_{\frac{3}{2}} + \ldots\ldots + y_{n-\frac{3}{2}} + y_{n-\frac{1}{2}} \right),$$

where $h = \dfrac{b-a}{n}$

> The formulae in **4** and **5** given in the exam formulae booklet but you will need to remember what the letters stand for.

5 Simpson's rule for n strips and $(n+1)$ ordinates, where n **is even**, is

$$\int_a^b y \, dx \approx \frac{1}{3} h \{(y_0 + y_n) + 4(y_1 + y_3 + \ldots\ldots + y_{n-1}) + 2(y_2 + y_4 + \ldots\ldots + y_{n-2})\}$$

where $h = \dfrac{b-a}{n}$

10

Worked example 1

The curve with equation $y = e^{2x} - 4$ is sketched below. The curve crosses the x-axis at the point $A(a, 0)$ and the y-axis at the point $B(0, b)$. The shaded region is bounded by the arc AB and the coordinate axes.

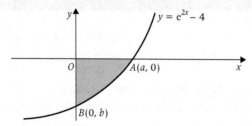

(a) Show that $a = \ln 2$ and state the value of b.

(b) The shaded region is rotated through 360° about the x-axis. Show that the volume of the solid formed is

$$\pi(16\ln 2 - 8.25)$$

(a) $A(a, 0)$ lies on curve $y = e^{2x} - 4 \Rightarrow 0 = e^{2a} - 4$

$\Rightarrow 4 = e^{2a} \Rightarrow 2a = \ln 4$ *Using Key point* **5** *in ch4:* $x = e^y \Leftrightarrow y = \ln x$.

$\Rightarrow a = \dfrac{1}{2}\ln 4 \Rightarrow a = \ln 4^{\frac{1}{2}} \Rightarrow a = \ln 2$ *Using* $k\ln x = \ln x^k$.

$B(0, b)$ lies on curve $y = e^{2x} - 4 \Rightarrow b = e^0 - 4 \Rightarrow b = -3$.

(b) Volume $= \displaystyle\int_0^{\ln 2} \pi(e^{2x} - 4)^2 \, dx$ *Using* **1**

$= \pi \displaystyle\int_0^{\ln 2} (e^{4x} - 8e^{2x} + 16) \, dx$

$= \pi\left[\dfrac{e^{4x}}{4} - \dfrac{8e^{2x}}{2} + 16x\right]_0^{\ln 2}$ *Using* $\displaystyle\int e^{kx} \, dx = \dfrac{1}{k}e^{kx} + c$.

$= \pi\left\{\left(\dfrac{e^{4\ln 2}}{4} - 4e^{2\ln 2} + 16\ln 2\right) - \left(\dfrac{1}{4} - 4 + 0\right)\right\}$

$= \pi\left\{\left(\dfrac{16}{4} - 4\times 4 + 16\ln 2\right) - \left(\dfrac{1}{4} - 4 + 0\right)\right\}$ *Using* $e^{p\ln q} = e^{\ln q^p} = q^p$.

$= \pi(16\ln 2 - 12 + 3.75) = \pi(16\ln 2 - 8.25)$

Worked example 2

The region R, bounded by the curve $y^2 = 4x$, the positive y-axis
and the line $y = 2$ is shown shaded in the diagram.

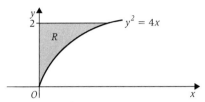

(a) Find the volume of the solid generated when the region R
is rotated through 2π radians about the y-axis.

(b) The region R is rotated through 2π radians about the x-axis.
Show that the volume of the solid generated is 2π.

(a) Volume $= \displaystyle\int_0^2 \pi \frac{y^4}{16}\, dy$

Using **2**, $y^2 = 4x \Rightarrow x^2 = \frac{y^4}{16}$.

$= \pi\left[\dfrac{y^5}{80}\right]_0^2$

$= \pi\left(\dfrac{32}{80} - 0\right) = \dfrac{2}{5}\pi$

(b) When $y = 2$, $x = 1$

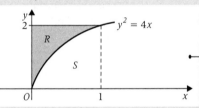

Find x where $y = 2$ cuts the curve.

Rotating regions about the x-axis,

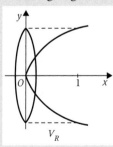 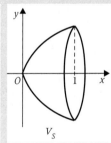 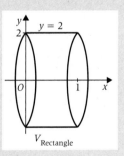

$V_R + V_S = V_{\text{Rectangle}}$

$V_{\text{Rectangle}}$ is same as volume
generated by rotating region
bounded by line $y = 2$ and the
positive coordinate axes =
volume of cylinder of
radius 2 height 1.

10

$$V_R + \int_0^1 \pi 4x \, dx = \int_0^1 \pi 2^2 \, dx$$

$$V_R + \pi \left[2x^2\right]_0^1 = \pi \left[4x\right]_0^1$$

$$V_R + 2\pi = 4\pi \Rightarrow V_R = 2\pi$$

> Using **1**

Worked example 3

Use the mid-ordinate rule with four strips of equal width to find an estimate for $\int_0^2 \dfrac{1}{2 + \sin x} \, dx$, giving your answer to three decimal places.

$$h = \frac{2 - 0}{4} = 0.5.$$

> Using **4** with $a = 0$, $b = 2$ and $n = 4$.

x-values $(x_{k+1} = x_k + h)$	Mid-x-values	Mid-ordinates $y = \dfrac{1}{2 + \sin x}$
$x_0 = 0$		
	$x_{\frac{1}{2}} = 0.25$	$y_{\frac{1}{2}} = \dfrac{1}{2 + \sin 0.25} = 0.44495\ldots$
$x_1 = 0.5$		
	$x_{\frac{3}{2}} = 0.75$	$y_{\frac{3}{2}} = \dfrac{1}{2 + \sin 0.75} = 0.37290\ldots$
$x_2 = 1$		
	$x_{\frac{5}{2}} = 1.25$	$y_{\frac{5}{2}} = \dfrac{1}{2 + \sin 1.25} = 0.33909\ldots$
$x_3 = 1.5$		
	$x_{\frac{7}{2}} = 1.75$	$y_{\frac{7}{2}} = \dfrac{1}{2 + \sin 1.75} = 0.33512\ldots$
$x_4 = 2$		

> Set calculator to radian mode.
>
> Always work to a greater degree of accuracy than the accuracy required (3 d.p.) for the final answer.

$$y_{\frac{1}{2}} + y_{\frac{3}{2}} + y_{\frac{5}{2}} + y_{\frac{7}{2}} = 1.49208\ldots$$

$$\int_0^2 \frac{1}{2 + \sin x} \, dx \approx h \left(y_{\frac{1}{2}} + y_{\frac{3}{2}} + y_{\frac{5}{2}} + y_{\frac{7}{2}}\right) = 0.5 \times 1.49208\ldots$$
$$= 0.74604\ldots$$

$$\int_0^2 \frac{1}{2 + \sin x} \, dx \approx 0.746 \text{ to three decimal places.}$$

Worked example 4

(a) Use Simpson's rule with five ordinates (four strips) to find an approximation to $\int_2^6 (\ln x)^2 \, dx$, giving your answer to three significant figures.

(b) Comment on how you could obtain a better approximation to the value of the integral using Simpson's rule.

$h = \dfrac{6-2}{4} = 1$

Using **5** with $a = 2$, $b = 6$ and $n = 4$.

x-values	$y = (\ln x)^2$
$x_0 = 2$	$y_0 = (\ln 2)^2 = 0.4804\ldots$
$x_1 = 3$	$y_1 = (\ln 3)^2 = 1.2069\ldots$
$x_2 = 4$	$y_2 = (\ln 4)^2 = 1.9218\ldots$
$x_3 = 5$	$y_3 = (\ln 5)^2 = 2.5902\ldots$
$x_4 = 6$	$y_4 = (\ln 6)^2 = 3.2104\ldots$

$$y_0 + y_4 = 3.6908\ldots$$
$$y_1 + y_3 = 3.7972\ldots$$
$$y_2 = 1.9218\ldots$$

(a) $\int_2^6 (\ln x)^2 \, dx \approx \dfrac{1}{3} h\{(y_0 + y_4) + 4(y_1 + y_3) + 2(y_2)\}$

$\approx \dfrac{1}{3} \times 1 \times \{3.6908\ldots + 4(3.7972\ldots) + 2(1.9218\ldots)\}$

$\approx \dfrac{1}{3} \times 1 \times \{22.7234\ldots\} = 7.5744\ldots$

$\int_2^6 (\ln x)^2 \, dx \approx 7.57$ to three significant figures.

(b) Increase the number of strips ensuring that the number of strips is even.

Using **3**

10

REVISION EXERCISE 10

1 The region R is bounded by the line $y = 6$, the coordinate axes and the line $x = 2$.

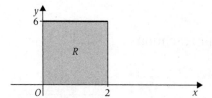

Find, as a multiple of π, the volume of the solid formed when R is rotated

(a) through 2π radians about the x-axis,

(b) through 2π radians about the y-axis.

2 Find, in terms of π, the volume of the solid generated by rotating the region bounded by the curve $y = \tan x$, the line $x = \dfrac{\pi}{4}$ and the x-axis from $x = 0$ to $x = \dfrac{\pi}{4}$ through 2π radians about the x-axis.

3 The shaded region bounded by the curve $y = e^x$, the line $x = \ln 5$ and the coordinate axes is rotated through $360°$ about the x-axis.

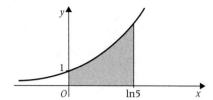

Find the volume of the solid generated, leaving your answer as a multiple of π.

4 The region R is bounded by the lines $y = x + 1$, $x = 1$ and the positive coordinate axes.

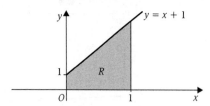

Find the volume of the solid formed when R is rotated
(a) through $360°$ about the x-axis,
(b) through $360°$ about the y-axis.

5 The region R, bounded by the curve $y = 1 - \tan x$ and the positive coordinate axes is shown shaded in the diagram.

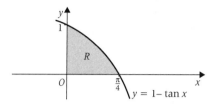

Find the volume of the solid generated when the region R is rotated through 2π radians about the x-axis. Give your answer to three significant figures.

6 A curve has equation $y = \sec 2x$.

   (a) Sketch the curve $y = \sec 2x$ for $-\dfrac{\pi}{4} < x < \dfrac{\pi}{4}$.

   (b) The region R is bounded by the curve, the coordinate axes and the line $x = \dfrac{1}{2}$. Find the volume of the solid generated when R is rotated through 2π radians about the x-axis, giving your answer to three significant figures.

7 The curve $x^2 + \dfrac{y^2}{4} = 1$ intersects the positive y-axis at the point A and intersects the positive x-axis at the point B.

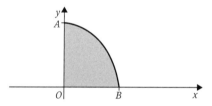

   (a) Find the coordinates of A and B.
   (b) The shaded region bounded by the arc AB and the positive coordinate axes is rotated through 2π radians about the y-axis. Find the volume of the solid formed.

10

8 The curve $y = x^{\frac{1}{2}}e^{-x}$ is defined for $x \geqslant 0$ and is sketched below. The point M is the maximum point of the curve.

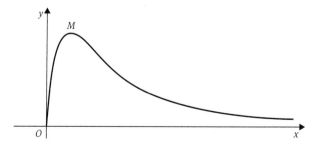

(a) Find the coordinates of M.

(b) **(i)** Find $\int xe^{-2x}\,dx$

(ii) The region enclosed by the curve, the x-axis and the line $x = 1$ is rotated through $360°$ about the x-axis. Find the volume of the solid generated, leaving your answer in terms of π and e.

9 Use the mid-ordinate rule with four strips of equal width to find an estimate for $\displaystyle\int_{2}^{6} (\ln x)^2\,dx$, giving your answer to three decimal places.

10 Use Simpson's rule with five ordinates (four strips) to find an approximation to $\displaystyle\int_{0}^{2} \frac{1}{2 + \sin x}\,dx$, giving your answer to three significant figures.

11 A curve has equation $y = \sqrt{(2 + e^x)}$. The region R is bounded by the curve, the coordinate axes and the line $x = 3$.

(a) Use the mid-ordinate rule with four strips of equal width to find an estimate for the area of R, giving your answer to two decimal places.

(b) Use Simpson's rule with seven ordinates (six strips) to find an estimate for the area of R, giving your answer to two decimal places.

(c) The region R is rotated through $360°$ about the x-axis. Find the volume of the solid generated, leaving your answer in terms of π and e.

12 (a) Use Simpson's rule with five ordinates (four strips) to find an approximation to $\displaystyle\int_{1}^{2} \ln\!\left(2 + \sqrt{x}\,\right) dx$, giving your answer to three decimal places.

(b) Comment on how you could obtain a better approximation to the value of the integral using Simpson's rule.

13 Given that the exact value of $\displaystyle\int_{0}^{1} 3^x\,dx = \frac{2}{\ln 3}$, determine which of the following two methods gives the better estimate for $\displaystyle\int_{0}^{1} 3^x\,dx$:

(a) Simpson's rule with five ordinates (four strips);

(b) the mid-ordinate rule with four strips of equal width.

14 The points $A(1, 1)$ and $B\left(4, \dfrac{1}{4}\right)$ lie on the curve $y = \dfrac{1}{x}$. The points C and D have coordinates $(4, 0)$ and $(1, 0)$ respectively.

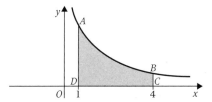

(a) The shaded region bounded by the arc AB, the lines $x = 1$ and $x = 4$ and the x-axis is rotated through $360°$ about the x-axis. Find the volume of the solid generated.

(b) The region bounded by the trapezium $ABCD$ is rotated through $360°$ about the x-axis.
Find the volume of the solid generated.

(c) Hence find the volume of the solid generated when the region bounded by the arc AB and the line segment AB is rotated through $360°$ about the x-axis.

Test yourself	What to review
	If your answer is incorrect:

1 The curve with equation $y = x\sqrt{x^2 + 4}$ is sketched below.

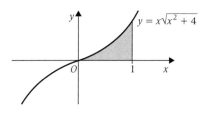

The shaded region bounded by the curve, the x-axis and the line $x = 1$ is rotated through $360°$ about the x-axis. Find the volume of the solid generated.

Review Advancing Maths for AQA C3C4 pages 163–167.

2 The region bounded by the curve $y = \ln x$, the coordinate axes and the line $y = 2$ is rotated through 2π radians about the y-axis. Find the volume of the solid formed, leaving your answer in terms of π and e.

Review Advancing Maths for AQA C3C4 pages 163–167.

3 Use the mid-ordinate rule with four strips of equal width to find an estimate for $\displaystyle\int_0^1 \cos x^2 \, dx$, giving your answer to three decimal places.

Review Advancing Maths for AQA C3C4 pages 168–172.

10

Test yourself (continued)	**What to review**

If your answer is incorrect:

4   Use Simpson's rule with five ordinates (four strips) to find an approximation to $\int_1^2 x^{x+1}\,dx$, giving your answer to three significant figures

Review Advancing Maths for AQA C3C4 pages 173–178.

Test yourself   **ANSWERS**

4 3.31

3 0.909

2 $\frac{\pi}{2}(e^4 - 1)$

1 $\frac{23}{15}\pi$

Exam style practice paper

Answer **all** questions.
Time allowed: 1 hour 30 minutes

1 Use the mid-ordinate rule with four strips of equal width to
find an estimate for $\int_2^4 \frac{1}{\ln x}\, dx$ giving your answer to three
significant figures.   *(4 marks)*

2 The functions f and g are defined with their respective
domains by

$$f(x) = \frac{2}{x-1} \text{ for real values of } x, x \neq 1$$

$$g(x) = x + 4 \text{ for real values of } x.$$

The composite function fg is denoted by h.
(a) (i) Find $h(x)$.   *(2 marks)*
    (ii) Find the maximum possible domain of h.   *(1 mark)*
(b) Find $h^{-1}(x)$, where h^{-1} is the inverse of h.   *(3 marks)*

3 (a) It is given that $x = \tan y$.

   (i) Find $\dfrac{dx}{dy}$ in terms of y.   *(1 mark)*

   (ii) Hence find $\dfrac{dy}{dx}$ in terms of x.   *(3 marks)*

  (b) A curve has equation $y = \tan^{-1} 2x$. Find the
       gradient of the curve at the point $\left(\dfrac{1}{2}, \dfrac{\pi}{4}\right)$.   *(3 marks)*

4 The graph of $y = x^3 - 2x + 1$ intersects the line
$y = 4 - x$ at the point where $x = \alpha$.
(a) Show that α satisfies the equation $x^3 = x + 3$.   *(1 mark)*
(b) Prove that α lies between 1.6 and 1.7.   *(2 marks)*

(c) Use the iteration $x_{n+1} = \sqrt[3]{x_n + 3}$ with $x_1 = 1.6$

    to find the values of x_2, x_3 and x_4, giving your
    answers to four significant figures.   *(3 marks)*

5 (a) Describe a sequence of two geometrical transformations that maps the graph of $y = |x|$ onto the graph of $y = 3 - |x|$.

(4 marks)

(b) On the same set of axes sketch the graphs of $y = 3 - |x|$ and $y = |2x - 2|$ indicating the coordinates of the points where the graphs cross the coordinate axes. Label your graphs with their equations. *(5 marks)*

(c) Solve the equation $3 - |x| = |2x - 2|$. *(3 marks)*

(d) Hence, or otherwise, solve the inequality $3 - |x| < |2x - 2|$. *(2 marks)*

6 A curve with equation $y = \dfrac{e^x}{\sqrt{e^x + 3}}$ is sketched below.

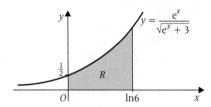

The region R bounded by the curve $y = \dfrac{e^x}{\sqrt{e^x + 3}}$, the x-axis

and the lines $x = 0$ and $x = \ln 6$ is shaded.

Using the substitution $u = e^x + 3$, or otherwise,

(a) find the area of R *(4 marks)*

(b) show that the volume of the solid formed when the region R is rotated through $360°$ about the x-axis is

$$\pi\left(5 + 3\ln\left(\frac{4}{9}\right)\right).$$

(4 marks)

7 (a) Differentiate $(4 + \cos x)^{\frac{1}{2}}$ with respect to x. *(2 marks)*

(b) Show that the equation of the normal to the curve

$$y = \frac{\sin x}{\sqrt{4 + \cos x}}$$ at the point on the curve where

$x = \dfrac{\pi}{2}$ is $2y + 8x = 4\pi + 1$ *(5 marks)*

8 (a) Prove the identity $\operatorname{cosec}^4 \theta - \cot^4 \theta = 2\operatorname{cosec}^2 \theta - 1$.

(3 marks)

(b) Hence, or otherwise, solve the equation $\operatorname{cosec}^4 2x - \cot^4 2x = 7$, giving all values of x in the interval $-180° < x < 180°$. *(5 marks)*

9 A curve is defined for $x > 0$ by the equation $y = x^2 \ln x$ and is sketched below.

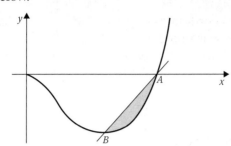

The curve crosses the x-axis at the point A and has a minimum point at B.

The region bounded by the curve and the line AB is shaded in the diagram.

(a) State the coordinates of A. *(1 mark)*

(b) Find the coordinates of B. *(5 marks)*

(c) (i) Use integration by parts to find $\int x^2 \ln x \, dx$.

(4 marks)

(ii) Show that the area of the shaded region is given by

$$-\int_{e^{-\frac{1}{2}}}^{1} x^2 \, \ln x \, dx - \frac{1}{4} \, e^{-\frac{3}{2}} \left(e^{\frac{1}{2}} - 1 \right)$$

(3 marks)

(iii) Hence find the area of the shaded region in terms of e. *(2 marks)*

Answers

Revision exercise 1

1 (a) 1 (b) 3 (c) $\dfrac{12}{3+a}$

2 (a) 8; –5 (b) 1; $\dfrac{2}{3}$

(b) Range is $-4 \leqslant h(x) \leqslant 5$

3 (a)

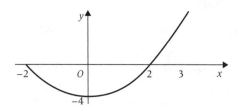

4 (a)

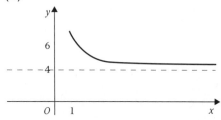

(b) $4 < p(x) \leqslant 6$

5 Range is $-\dfrac{1}{2} \leqslant f(x) \leqslant 1$.

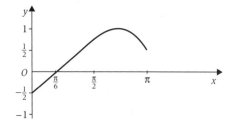

6 Range is $0 \leqslant g(x) \leqslant 2$

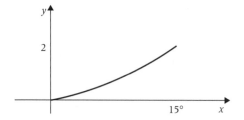

7 (a) (i) $h(x) = x^2 + 2$

    (ii) $h(x) \geqslant 2$

(b) (i) $p(x) = (x+3)^2 - 1$

    (ii) $p(x) \geqslant -1$

8 (a) f is not one-one

(b) (i) g is one-one; $g^{-1}(x) = \sqrt{x-3}$

    (ii) $x > 7$.

9 (a) $h(x) = \dfrac{4}{x+2} - 5$

(b) (i) $h^{-1}(x) = \dfrac{4}{x+5} - 2$

    (ii) real values of $h^{-1}(x) \neq -2$

10 (a) $f^{-1}(x) = \dfrac{4}{x} - 3$; $g^{-1}(x) = \dfrac{2x + 4}{x - 3}$ **(b)** $x = 1, x = -4$

  (c) **(i)** range of f: real values of f(x), $f(x) \neq 0$; domain of f^{-1}: real values of x, $x \neq 0$

      (ii) range of g: real values of g(x), $g(x) \neq -3$; domain of g^{-1}: real values of x, $x \neq -3$

  (d) $f(g(x)) = \dfrac{2x - 4}{3x - 1}$

11 (a) **(i)** $f(x) \leq 5$ **(b)** $g^{-1}(x) = \dfrac{2}{x} + 4$ range of g^{-1}: real values

      (ii) f is not one-one so does not have an inverse   of $g^{-1}(x)$, $g^{-1}(x) \neq 4$

  (c) **(i)** $h(x) = \dfrac{2}{1 - x^2}$ **(ii)** real values of x, $x \neq \pm 1$

12 (a) $h(x) = \dfrac{12}{3x - 2} - 3$ **(b)** $h^{-1}(x) = \dfrac{4}{x + 3} + \dfrac{2}{3} = \dfrac{2(x + 9)}{3(x + 3)}$;

                                                           range is real values of $h^{-1}(x) > 1$.

13 (a)

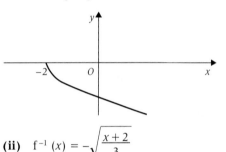

                                              (b) **(i)** f is one-one since domain consists
                                                        of only negative values of x;

                                                (ii) $f^{-1}(x) = -\sqrt{\dfrac{x + 2}{3}}$

14 (a) **(i)** $h(x) = 9 - \dfrac{5}{x - 3}$ **(b)** **(ii)** real values of x, $x \neq 0$

      (ii) real values of x, $x \neq 3$ **(c)** $x = 1$; $x = \dfrac{1}{5}$

Revision exercise 2

1 (a) $y = (x - 3)^3 + 2$ **(b)** $y = 1 + \sin\left(\dfrac{x}{3}\right)$ **(c)** $y = -2^{x+1}$

2 (a) Stretch of SF 0.5 in x-direction; stretch of SF 3 in y-direction

  (b) Translation $\begin{bmatrix} 1 \\ 4 \end{bmatrix}$

  (c) Stretch of SF 2 in x-direction; translation of 2 units in y-direction

3 (a) Translation of $\begin{bmatrix} 1 \\ 0 \end{bmatrix}$; stretch of SF 4 in y-direction

  (b) Stretch of SF $\dfrac{1}{5}$ in y-direction; translation 7 units in y-direction

4 Two-way stretch SF 3 in x-direction and SF $\dfrac{1}{8}$ in y-direction

5 Translation $\begin{bmatrix} 1 \\ -2 \end{bmatrix}$; stretch SF 4 in *y*-direction

6 (a)
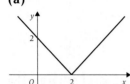
(b)
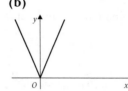
(c)
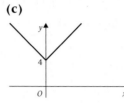
(d)
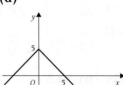

7 (a)
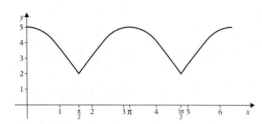
(b)
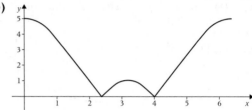

8 (a)
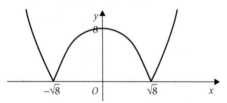

9 (a) $\frac{2}{3}$; 8 **(b)** 1; $\frac{2}{5}$

(b) 2, –2, 2 $\sqrt{3}$, –2 $\sqrt{3}$

10 (a)
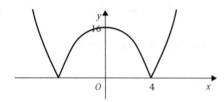

11 (a)
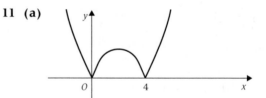

(b) 3, –3, $\sqrt{23}$, – $\sqrt{23}$

(c) $x < -\sqrt{23}$, –3 < x < 3, x > $\sqrt{23}$

(b) (i) 3, 6 **(ii)** 3 < x < 6

12 (a)
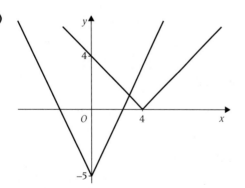

(b) –9, 3 **(c)** –9 < x < 3

13 **(a)** $f(x) \geqslant 0$; $g(x) \geqslant 1$

(b) Neither f nor g has an inverse since they are not one-one.

(c) **(i)** $|x^2 - 2|$ **(ii)** $1, -1, \sqrt{3}, -\sqrt{3}$

(d) $-2 < x < 1$

Revision exercise 3

1 **(a)** $B(0, 1)$ **(b)**

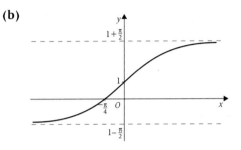

2 **(a)** Translation $\begin{bmatrix} 1 \\ 0 \end{bmatrix}$ **(b)** $A(1, 0)$ $B\left(0, -\dfrac{\pi}{4}\right)$ **(c)** **(i)**   **(ii)** 1

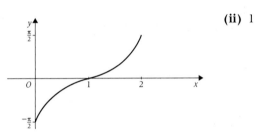

3 **(a)** $\dfrac{\pi}{2}$ **(b)** 0 **(c)** $\dfrac{2}{3}$ **(d)** $\dfrac{\sqrt{5}}{3}$

4 $-\dfrac{4}{3}$

5 **(a)** Stretch in x-direction scale factor $\dfrac{1}{2}$, translation $\begin{bmatrix} 1 \\ 0 \end{bmatrix}$ **6** $10°, 30°$

(b) π **7** $50°, 110°, 170°$

(c)   **8** $45°, 165°, 225°, 345°$

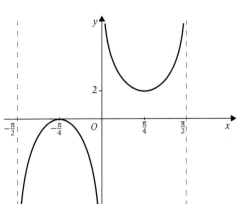

9 (a)

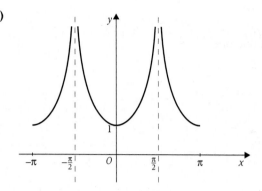

10   63°, 117°, 243°, 297°

11 (b)   0.79, 2.68, 3.93, 5.82

12 (a)   1.23, 5.05 **(c)** 1.23, 1.98, 4.30, 5.05

13 (c)   ±9°, ±81°

14 (a)   2.68, 5.82 **(c)** 0.588, 2.68, 3.73, 5.82

15 (c)   0.253, 2.89, 3.48, 5.94

16   100°, 220°, 340°

Revision exercise 4

1 (a) $\ln 5$ **(b)** $-\ln 2, \ln 3$ **2 (a)** $\frac{1}{3}e^6$ **(b)** $e; e^2$ **3 (a)** 16 **(b)** $y = 16x - 3$ **4** $9e^{3x}$; minimum.

5 $5; x + 5y = 20$

6 (a) $\frac{1}{3}(1 - e^{-3})$ **(b)** $\ln 2 + \frac{39}{2}$ **(c)** $e^9 - 2e^{-6} + 1$

7 (a) $\left(\frac{1}{2}\ln 2, 9 - 2\ln 2\right)$; minimum **(b)** $\frac{19}{2} - \frac{1}{2}e^{-2}$

8 (a) $\frac{dy}{dx} = -1 + 3e^{-x}, \frac{d^2y}{dx^2} = -3e^{-x}$ **(b)** $(\ln 3, 5 - \ln 3)$; maximum

9 (a)

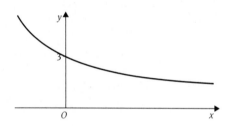

(b) $3y = x + 9$; $(-9,0)$ **(c)** $\frac{1}{3}(7 - e^{-3})$

10 (a) $\frac{1}{2}e$ **(b) (i)** -2 **(ii)** $y = 2 - 2x$

11 (a) $f'(x) < 0$ when $x > 0$ **(b)** $f(x) > -3$

(c) $2\ln 2 + \frac{1}{3e^{-3}} - \frac{1}{3e^{-6}} - 3$

12 (a) $(0,4)$ **(b) (i)** $x + 2y - 8$ **(ii)** $(8,0)$

(c) (i) $5x - 2e^{\frac{x}{2}}$ + constant **(ii)** $24 - 10\ln 5$

13 (a) (i) $(0,-7)$

(b) (i)

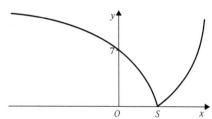

(ii) $0, \frac{1}{2}\ln\frac{23}{9}$

(c) $32\ln 2 - 16\ln 3 + \frac{7}{2}$

14 (a) **(i)** f(x) > 2 **(ii)** $\frac{1}{4}\ln\left(\frac{x-2}{3}\right)$ **15 (b)** (1, 3); $\left(\frac{3}{2}, \frac{7}{4} + 3\ln\frac{3}{2}\right)$

(b) **(i)** $x + 12y = 60$ **(ii)** $\frac{1}{4}(3e - 1)$

Revision exercise 5

1 (a) $2x + 4\cos x$ **(b)** $e^x - 5\sin x$ **(c)** $2\cos x + 3\sin x$

2 (a) $\frac{dy}{dx} = 4\cos x - 5\sin x$ **(b)** $y = 4x + 2$ **3 (a) (i)** $-5\sin x - 7$ **(ii)** $-12 \leqslant f'(x) \leqslant -2$

4 (a) $15(3x + 4)^4$ **(b)** $12x(x^2 + 7)^5$ **(c)** $2(4x + 5)^{-\frac{1}{2}}$ **(d)** $8(5x + 1)(5x^2 + 2x - 3)^3$ **(e)** $\frac{3}{3x + 7}$

(f) $3(x + 1)(x^2 + 2x + 5)^{\frac{1}{2}}$ **(g)** $6e^{3x} - 12(x + 1)^3$ **(h)** $\frac{x}{\sqrt{1 + x^2}}$

5 (a) $-12\sin 2x$ **(b)** $42\cos 6x$ **(c)** $21\cos 3x - 15\sin 5x$ **(d)** $4e^{4x-5}$ **(e)** $\cos x \, e^{\sin x}$ **(f)** $\frac{\sin x}{2 - \cos x}$

6 (a) $y = 1 - \frac{2}{\sqrt{x + 3}}$ **(b)** $(1, -12)$

7 (a) $\frac{dy}{dx} = 6x(x^2 + 5)^{-\frac{1}{2}} - 2x$ **(b)** $(-2, 14), (0, 6\sqrt{5}), (2, 14)$ **8 (a)** 7 **(b)** $x + 7y = 8$

9 (a) $\frac{1}{3y(y + 2)}$ **(b)** $\frac{1}{4\cos(y - 1)}$ **(c)** $\frac{-1}{6y\sin(y^2 + 1)}$ **10 (b)** $2y + \frac{3}{y} + \cos(y - 1)$ **(c)** $6y - x - 1 = 0$

Revision exercise 6

1 (a) $3x^2 \ln x + x^2$ **(b)** $e^{5x}(5\cos x - \sin x)$ **(c)** $2(x^2 - 3x)\cos 2x + (2x - 3)\sin 2x$

(d) $e^{2x}\left(2\ln x + \frac{1}{x}\right)$ **(e)** $x^3(4\cos 3x - 3x\sin 3x)$ **(f)** $4\cos 4x \cos 3x - 3\sin 4x \sin 3x$

2 (a) $\frac{e^{2x}(2x - 1)}{x^2}$ **(b)** $\frac{-(x + 1)\sin x - \cos x}{(x + 1)^2}$ **(c)** $\frac{1 - 3\ln x}{x^4}$ **(d)** $\frac{x^2(3\sin 2x - 2x\cos 2x)}{(\sin 2x)^2}$

(e) $\frac{x + 2}{2(x + 1)\sqrt{x + 1}}$ **(f)** $\frac{x(2\ln x - 1)}{(\ln x)^2}$

5 (a) $\frac{(x + 3)(1 - 3x)}{(1 + x^2)^2}$ **(b)** $\left(-3, -\frac{1}{2}\right)$ minimum; $\left(\frac{1}{3}, \frac{9}{2}\right)$ maximum

6 $(-1, e)$; maximum

7 (a) $\frac{5x(x + 4)}{2\sqrt{x + 5}}$ **(b)** $(0,0), (-4, 16)$

8 (a) $-4x(2\ln x + 1)$ **(b)** $4x + y = 5$ **(c)** $\left(e^{-\frac{1}{2}}, 1 + 2e^{-1}\right)$ **(d)** -8

9 (b) $y = x + 1$

10 (b) $\frac{5 - 6\ln x}{x^4}$ **(c)** $\left(e^{\frac{1}{2}}, \frac{2e - 1}{2e}\right)$; minimum

Revision exercise 7

3 (a) (i)

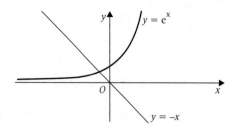

(b) −0.368, −0.692

4 (b) 1.82, 1.79

5 (b) (ii) 1.26, 1.14
 (c) cobweb convergence

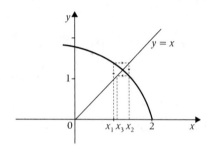

6 (b) (ii) 1.817, 1.871, 1.855   **7 (a)** 2.218   **(b)** $x = 2(1 + e^{-x})$

8 (c) 2.05; 2.16
 (d) staircase convergence

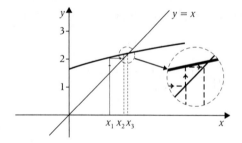

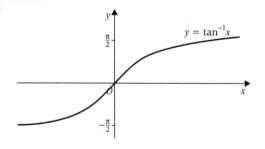

9 (a)

(b) (i)

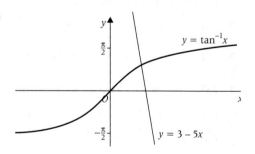

 (c) (ii) 0.5061

Revision exercise 8

1 **(a)** $\frac{1}{3}(2x-1)^9 + c$ **(b)** $\frac{2}{3}$ **2 (a) (i)** $\frac{1}{2}e^{2x} + c$ **(ii)** $-\frac{1}{2}e^{-2x} + c$ **(b)** $\frac{1}{2}e - 1 - \frac{1}{2}e^{-1}$

3 0.959 **4 (a)** $\tan x + c$ **(b)** $\tan x - x + c$ **(c)** $\tan x - 2\ln|\sec x| + c$

5 **(a)** $-2\cot 2x + c$ **(b)** $-2\cot 2x - 4x + c$ **6** $\frac{1}{6}$

7 **(a)** $3x^2 + 9$ **(b)** $\frac{1}{3}\ln(x^3 - 9x) + c$ **8 (a) (i)** $\ln|\sec x| + c$ **(ii)** $-\ln|1 + \cos x| + c$ **9 (a)** $\frac{1}{x}$

10 **(a)** $2\ln(e^{2x} + 2) + c$ **(b)** $\ln 4$ **11** $\frac{1}{90}(9x + 1)(x - 1)^9 + c$ **12** $-\frac{1}{6}\cos^6 x + c$

13 **(a)** $2(x^2 + 3)^{\frac{5}{2}} + c$ **(b)** $-\frac{1}{2}\cos(x^2 + 3) + c$ **(c)** $\frac{1}{5}(x^2 + 3)^{\frac{5}{2}} - (x^2 + 3)^{\frac{3}{2}} + c$

14 $\frac{1}{3}e^{(x^3 + 3x)} + c$ **15** $e^x + 2 - 2\ln(e^x + 2) + c$ [or $e^x - 2\ln(e^x + 2) + k$] **16** $\frac{7}{3}$

17 -0.143 **18** $e - 1 + \ln\left(\frac{2}{e + 1}\right)$ **19** $\frac{7}{6}$ **20** $\frac{11}{24}$

Revision exercise 9

1 $x \sin x + \cos x + c$ **2** $xe^x - e^x + c$ **3** $\frac{1}{4}x^2(2\ln x - 1) + c$ **4** $\frac{1}{4}$ **6** 0.3818 **7** $\pi - 2$ **8** 2e

10 $\frac{1}{6}(3e^2 + 11)$ **11 (b)** $4\ln 2 - \frac{15}{16}$ **12 (a)** $\tan^{-1}x + c$ **(b)** $\frac{1}{2}\ln(1 + x^2) + c$

Revision exercise 10

1 **(a)** 72π **(b)** 24π **2** $\pi\left(1 - \frac{\pi}{4}\right)$ **3** 12π **4 (a)** $\frac{7}{3}\pi$ **(b)** $\frac{5}{3}\pi$ **5** 0.964

6 **(a)**   **(b)** 2.45

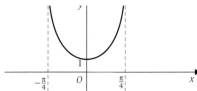

7 **(a)** A(0,2) B(1,0) **(b)** $\frac{4}{3}\pi$

8 **(a)** $\left(\frac{1}{2}, \frac{1}{\sqrt{2e}}\right)$ **(b) (i)** $-\frac{1}{2}xe^{-2x} - \frac{1}{4}e^{-2x} + c$ **(ii)** $\frac{1}{4}\pi(1 - 3e^{-2})$

9 7.577 **10** 0.749 **11 (a)** 8.26 **(b)** 8.30 **(c)** $(5 + e^3)\pi$.

12 **(a)** 1.168 **(b)** Increase the number of steps (strips)

13 Simpson's rule (1.8205...) gives a better estimate than the mid-ordinate rule (1.8147...) for the exact value

$\frac{2}{\ln 3}$ ($= 1.8204...$)

14 **(a)** $\frac{3}{4}\pi$ **(b)** $\frac{21}{16}\pi$ **(c)** $\frac{9}{16}\pi$

Exam style practice paper

1 1.91

2 **(a)** **(i)** $h(x) = \dfrac{2}{x+3}$ **(ii)** real values of x, $x \neq -3$ **(b)** $h^{-1}(x) = \dfrac{2}{x} - 3$

3 **(a)** **(i)** $\sec^2 y$ **(ii)** $\dfrac{1}{1+x^2}$ **(b)** 1

4 **(c)** $x_2 = 1.663$, $x_3 = 1.671$, $x_4 = 1.672$

5 **(a)** Reflection in the x-axis then translation $\begin{bmatrix} 0 \\ 3 \end{bmatrix}$ **(b)**

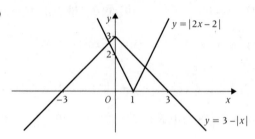

(c) $x = -\dfrac{1}{3}$, $x = \dfrac{5}{3}$ **(d)** $x < -\dfrac{1}{3}$, $x > \dfrac{5}{3}$

6 **(a)** 2

7 **(a)** $-\dfrac{1}{2} \sin x \, (4 + \cos x)^{-\frac{1}{2}}$

8 **(b)** $x = \pm 15°, \pm 75°, \pm 105°, \pm 165°$

9 **(a)** $(1, 0)$ **(b)** $\left(e^{-\frac{1}{2}}, -\dfrac{1}{2e} \right)$

(c) **(i)** $\dfrac{1}{3} x^3 \ln x - \dfrac{1}{9} x^3 + c$ **(iii)** $\dfrac{1}{36} \left(4 - 9e^{-1} - e^{-\frac{3}{2}} \right)$